It's On My Wall!

Edited by

Robert W. Olmsted

Northwoods Press

Copyright © 1989 Northwoods Press, for the authors included. All rights returned to authors following publication.

ISBN 0-89002-297-6   paper $9.95
ISBN 0-89002-298-4   cloth $19.95

Welcome to the third annual CAL Anthology entitled IT'S ON MY WALL! Participation in this anthology is open to all. The book is produced by the dues and donations of members of The Conservatory of American Letters, a non profit, tax exempt, literary/educational foundation. We welcome people interested in our purpose to join the Conservatory and support our programs so that other noncommercial, but well crafted literary art can be conserved for future generations. Send a self addressed .45 stamped envelope to CAL to learn how you can participate in many CAL programs, including the next Anthology.

CAL's editorial address is PO Box 88, Thomaston, Maine 04861

IT'S ON MY WALL! is dedicated to the Patron Members of the Conservatory Of American Letters

Contents

Everett Whealdon
Port Townsend, WA

Apple Blossom Homestead

The tree stood in the corner of the meadow
where the river bends west.
"There used to be five," grandfather said,
"planted years ago by a priest.
He told me, himself, how he bedded the seeds.
Well, the bank caved in as the river moved over;
now there's only one left, maybe 75 or 80 years old."

An old apple tree, hung full of moss, dead limbs,
birds' nests, cobwebs, dried leaves.
The trunk, a foot and a half thick;
bark covered with woodpecker holes.
Dropped fruit from high up live limbs
got bruised.

"There's a fresh one, sonny,
the horses eat most of 'em;
they're not much for color, but crisp and juicy."
That very same winter,
when the river rose with a January freshet,
bank and tree washed away;
swept downriver like the others.

Old timers along the lower Columbia
knew the story.
About the time the first wagons rolled west
a Chinese ship went aground on Peacock Spit
hard by the bar, where, 300 years after Columbus,
Captain Gray's ship Columbia
sailed across and named the river.

Some of the crew still alive;
one little girl whose parents both died
on the long, stormy voyage after the ship,
blown off course, rigging wrecked, drifted with wind and current.
Old Doctor John, the 'eagle man',

(more)

chief at Fort Vancouver, took care of stragglers,
Indians, Missouri immigrants, Chinese.

Young Father Sean, Jesuit Priest,
came overland with a fur brigade.
Started a mission school,
got acquainted with the little Chinese girl,
and, as the years went by, got better acquainted
with the girl whose name was Apple Blossom.
One Chinese sailor had been promised little Apple Blossom
by her parents before they died.
This one, nicknamed Buck—and so he was known
everywhere he went, his Chinese name forgotten—
never forgot the promise.
Father Sean taught the Faith to Apple Blossom.
By the time she was fifteen he knew he was in love.
A priest is still a man, he argued;
a man must choose his path.
But I chose my path, I made vows;
now must I spoil it all?
She's betrothed to another, she says.
May he come to claim her?
And does she love me?

Apple Blossom loved his teaching, loved him, too.
She knew she was beautiful and attractive;
everybody at the fort let her know it.
As for that Buck—she, too, forgot his Chinese name.

Several years they lived in the little valley
tucked away in the Coast Range,
where they could hear the ocean roar during storms.
They built a cabin near the site
of the Indian Village
where the Chinooks—fewer, always fewer- lived.

'Papa Sean' and 'Pomme Tipso' were welcome.
Sean learned the Old Chinook language;

(more)

He showed his neighbors how to raise potatoes,
they showed him how to catch and smoke salmon.
Apple Blossom learned to bake bread
and be content in the long, rainy winters.
The apple trees bore fruit.
Grandfather came overland, a boy of sixteen.
His folks staked a farm in the Willamette Valley,
but granddad took to wandering.
At Fort Vancouver he heard about Father Sean and Apple Blossom,
and set out to find them.

Down the Columbia and across to the bay, he
followed the tide up the little river to the Chinook village.
There was a first time and a last time;
over the years there were several times.
Apple Blossom and Sean always welcomed him.

Buck, the Chinese sailor, handy man on any ship,
went north to Vancouver Island, south to California.
Arrived in time to join the gold rush.
Prospecting in the mountain willderness
of Northern California he found gold.
Looking for his Apple Blossom bride,
Buck came back to Fort Vancouver.
"Too late, my friend, she's flown away,
and the church has lost a priest."
But Buck had the contract in his heart,
and knew that Apple Blossom knew it, too.
Up the winding little river, he, also, rode the tide.

He found them making garden on a fresh spring day;
Apple Blossom, still a fine young woman,
and Irish Sean, with his great, black beard
and strong, supple frame.
Buck was not put off, he told them why he'd come.
Answered Sean: "Have I left my calling,
renounced my claim to heaven,

(more)

and must I now be asked to give my love up too?
Damned I may be, but double damned if I will.''

The Chinese sailor had crossed the wide Pacific
under adverse—to put it mildly—circumstances.
He held his own in mining camps,
knifed his way through tong wars.
He sized the situation, seized on the answer.
The knife flashed, a catlike leap, feint, dive thrust,
and Sean lay bleeding on the grass withApple Blossom
crouching by his side, too stunned to cry or speak.
Were Sean's lips moving? Did his hand cross his chest?

Now Chinook Chief Kensell and two others
ran into the clearing,
trader's guns in hand. Shots.
Buck ducked, ran, made it to the trees by the river;
jumped into his canoe and got away.

That same day, coming upriver to visit his friends,
grandfather passed the Chinaman coming down.
Strange, he thought, seems in a devil of a hurry.
His friends' cabin was deserted;
he found Apple Blossom, ill and shaking,
in Chief Kensell's longhouse.
"He'll come back, I know, perhaps bring others.
I must get away, but where, and how?"

"We went to San Francisco,"
(grandfather always finished the story up short).
"She remembered enough about her parents
to find people there who belonged to her 'tong', or clan.
They took her in.''

Stuart Bartow
Danbury, CT

Seated Alone In An Old House

A cicada releases his shrill and shapeless cry
That can be possessed by no one.
This wooden house seems to have suddenly erupted around me.
Dusk has been allowed to creep in
Like a gentle, dreamless sleep.
The clock is now a pulsebeat,
The refrigerator a large,
Dull man who waits to be greeted.

Crickets are calling each other from behind the wall
And under the floorboards,
Scraping their wings
Like ghostly violins,
Ventriloquists of the hidden places.

I would like to throw my voice
Through the distances of minutes,
Through the immense wilderness of words
That lies between two people,
To say how much love I have for life,
This life,
In this warm room lit by the mystery of electricity
and the unearthly light of thousands
Of tiny eyes.

Stuart Bartow
Danbury, CT

Dream Of Tiny Deer

Nothing had changed
Except the deer had shrunk to the size of young squirrels
In spring.
Graceful as ever
Now they could glide more gently through the woods
Their hooves scattering drowsy complaints
From the leaves.

Now they could hide in ferns
And in tree hollows wait
Out winter gales
Though the life of endless running
Remained theirs
The tips of their antlers barely brushing
The surfaces
Our knees plough through
As we sleep.

Flinging their lithe bodies through drifts
Hooves hardly scar the snow
Darting between bushes
And through branches of saplings
Like alien
Insect arms reaching out of the snow
Fingers of the muted witnesses
Who dream also
Of touching deer.

Sylvia Spotts
Columbia, MO

Lunchpails

The smell of ripened grapes
on sun-steeped vines
pulls up from out the past
an entire reality
having nothing to do with today,
but a lifetime ago:

The schoolyard, the teacher's dress,
the strident sounds
of dirty boys in knickers.
And always the lunchpails
filled with grape-jelly sandwiches —
all brought back
as the children echo down the years
in a mother's dreams,
or the rolling of distant thunder
brings back the bombs
of a wartime long-since gone,
and all but forgotten.

So easily tumbled together
the days are blurred,
with always and ever the lunchpails
filled with yesterdays —
the peelings and crumbs we carry
down the flow of our years.

Craig Kowalkowski
Milwaukee, WI

The Short Happy Ride

Ernest Ernest
instead of mouthing a shotgun
& pulling the trigger
you should have driven west
to the Grand Canyon
on a chopped Harley hog
dressed in studded leather & hip shades
& black biker boots.
Yes, you should have driven west
with all your unfinished manuscripts
in your old Italian army sack.
You should have raced, yes,
along the west rim past Maricopa Point
past Mohave Point
past Pima Point
past No Return Point
all the way to Hermit's Rest & then
right off the edge
your big black Harley roaring at 110.
Your chrome wheels
would have spun & spun
in the hot Arizona sunset.
Newsmen with *aficionado*
would have watched you plunge
millions of years
into the Grand abyss.
Ernest Ernest
what a way to go!

Peter Broner
Salt Point, NY

Nina

What The Soldiers Said

The barracks lay neatly arranged around a central parade ground like match boxes on the palm of a hand: neat, flat and monotonous, but now the *Kaserne* (one of Hitler's many, though built for his own goose-stepping troops, not foreign victorious soldiers) lay in darkness, only a few lights pointing the way among the symmetrically arranged buildings whose brightly lit windows stared with monotonous regularity into the dark night. It was the boring, empty hour before taps when the hallways reverberated hollowly and time seemed to stand still — 2100 hours of an evening in Germany in September 1946.

That was why they all looked up eagerly when Harry entered: not only the fat soldier lying idly on his bunk, his fat belly eased sideways to reduce the strain, tracing bored patterns with his forefinger or the reading soldier who sat cross-legged on his bunk with a magazine propped on his knees but even Pat, lying on his stomach, though he was busy writing a letter on a piece of cardboard that kept buckling in the middle — all of them looking up with expectation and surprise too when Harry entered because they had not expected him back so soon, his pass being good until midnight which he had loudly advertised to all and sundry; Harry looking now not quite as sure of himself as usual, his face flushed with beer, his cap pushed low into his neck, his Eisenhower jacket wide open, though his tie was still tucked into hir shirt.

"Hey, look who's comin'!" the fat soldier cried, raising himself on his arm. "If it ain't Capistrano in person."

"Casanova," the reading soldier corrected.

The fat soldier ignored the correction. "What's the matter, Harry?" he cried. "She stand you up?"

"Who me?" Harry said gloomily, sitting down on the fat soldier's bunk. Seeing the fat soldier's unprotected buttock his hand shot out and twisted a chunk of flesh between his thumb and forefinger.

"Hey, what's the idea?" the fat soldier yelled, rearing up like a stallion.

Harry jumped away. "Mustn't ask so many questions," he

lectured from a safe distance.

lectured from a safe distance.

"Fuck you too," the fat soldier said, rubbing his flank.

Harry sat down on the reading soldier's bunk and fumbled a cigarette out of his pocket.

"The bitch," he exhaled with gloomy amazement with the first puff. "She really stood me up."

The fat soldier let out a jeering guffaw. He had turned around on his bunk the better to see Harry.

"You can't make 'em all," the reading soldier said. "Besides, "I told you she wasn't worth botherin' with."

"To hell with you," Harry said. "You got your little Greatshen now or you'd sure as hell still bother with her yourself."

"What, you know her too?" the fat soldier inquired curiously.

"No, I wouldn't," the reading soldier said. "I got tired of her."

Harry was shaking his head. "Just slipped out and went home," he muttered.

"You laid her too?" the fat soldier insisted.

"Christ, who hasn't?" the reading soldier said.

"I haven't," the fat soldier said naively.

"Any guy who goes into the joint where she works has a better than even chance to come out with her," the reading soldier said.

"No kiddin'," the fat soldier said enviously. "Where does she work?"

"And she stands *me* up," Harry said. "Godd-a-m!"

"Will you guys pipe down, please?" Pat called from his bunk. "I'm trying to write a letter."

"Fuck off, will ya!" Harry called back without venom.

"How much she ask anyway?" the fat soldier now wanted to know.

"Nothin'. She ain't that kind of whore," the reading soldier said. "She fucks for the pleasure of it."

"Godd-a-m!" the fat soldier said. "She must be good."

"There wouldn't be so many guys crowdin' round her if she wasn't," the reading soldier said with some pride. "Though I got tired of her."

"Sh-i-i-t," Harry muttered.

"Where's she work?" the fat soldier asked again.

"Wouldn't you like to know," Harry said annoyed.

"Fuck off," the fat soldier exclaimed.

"What happened anyway?" the reading soldier asked Harry.

"Nothin' happened!" Harry exclaimed. "She wasn't even in. Where is she? I asked the boss. You mean Nina? the Kraut says, Nina gone home — Nina not feel vell. . . sh-i-i-t," he muttered again.

"Nina?" Pat asked across the room.

"Yeah," Harry said.

"You sure that's her name?" Pat wanted to know.

"Sure I'm sure," Harry said. "The bitch."

"Does she work at *The Golden Lion?*" Pat insisted.

"So that's where she works!" the fat soldier exclaimed.

"Don't tell me you're tryin' to make her too," the reading soldier teased.

"The bitch," Harry said, getting up, "the goddam cock-teasin' bitch."

The others got up too. It was almost lights-out time. Only Pat sat without moving.

What Nina Said

"You're such a serious fellow, Pat. Why don't you laugh a little more? You haven't even smiled. You've done nothing but growl at me all evening — well, almost all evening. Come on, laugh, why don't you laugh a little, Pat? Wasn't it good?. . .

"Come on. Just once. Or I'll tickle you. Come on, laugh just once to please me. I'll tickle you if you don't. There — and there. . .

"Okay, I give up, I give up, you won. But you laughed, you sure laughed. And how nice you look when you laugh, like a *Lausbub.* Do you know what a *Lausbub* is?. . .

"I didn't think you did. But you're a *Lausbub.* I'll call you *Lausbub* from now on. Like my boy. He's a *Lausbub* too. How old are you, Pat?. . .

"Twenty-two! And my boy is eleven. And the girl nine. You couldn't be their father, could you? And to think I only met you two days ago. Do you know how old I am?. . .

"Add ten years, Pat. Ten years. . .

"He was thirty when he was killed. In action. In Italy, in 1944. . .

"No, I don't mind talking about him. He was the best husband a girl could have. If he hadn't been such a happy-go-lucky fellow, maybe he'd still be alive today. But that was Ernst, always laughing, always taking things lightly. Not like you, *Lausbub*. If he'd only been a bit more serious. When he went to volunteer, Don't go, Ernst, don't go, I pleaded with him. What do you want me to do, Nina? he said, you know they'll draft me before long anyway, this way I'll have a jump on them. I knew he wouldn't come back. I felt it in every bone. But I'm boring you. . .

"Well, if you want me to. The last time he came home on furlough — for Easter — he came with a whole knapsack of goodies. You know, things we couldn't get any more. Delicacies. And nylons too. I ran around the whole neighborhood showing them off. You should have seen how everyone envied me. A fine husband you have, they said, patting me on the back, a wonderful husband. While my heart sank like a stone. What good were all those things to me? what good that he was faithful and didn't run around with other women? With me I wanted him to be, in bed at night when I cried my eyes out and the children asked: Where's daddy? We want our daddy, where's our daddy?

"He never wanted to believe that he wouldn't come back. He took me in his arms and told me about the war, the dead and the wounded, but for himself he didn't believe it. I'm coming back, Nina, don't forget, I'm coming back, he'd say. Like a rock he thought he could fly through all the shooting. While I felt his death in every bone. Oh God, how stupid men are! Someone hoists a catchy banner and they stagger after it like drunks until they're dead and then consider themselves heroes into the bargain. And when someone only so much as breathed a word about how silly it all was, they got thrown in prison. That's a fact. One of my neighbors once said something against the war and next day a hulking Gestapo man stood in front of her door. Just let me bring my kids to my mother, she begged. Not a chance. She had to come along right away.

"The same thing almost happened to me after I received the news. The summer wasn't over yet when a telegram arrived. Third Regiment. I knew right away what it was. I didn't even have to open the envelope anymore. Everything went blank in front of my eyes. I just barely managed to drag myself to the couch.

"When I came to my boy was standing next to me with the telegram in his hand. I found this on the floor, mommy, he said. I pulled him to me and burst out crying and held on to him so hard I hurt him. Let go, mommy, he screamed scared. But I wouldn't, my arms were like paralyzed, I didn't know what I was doing anymore. He started crying because he was scared and we both cried until my little girl came running into the room and hid trembling under the table, crying too. The whole house heard us.

"When I finally went out again I couldn't hold my tongue any longer. I began to curse the war, I didn't care who heard me. Control yourself, one of my neighbors whispered to me, or you'll wind up in a concentration camp. I shut up then. Not for me. I didn't give a damn for myself anymore but for the kids. What would they do without me? I couldn't even bring them to my mother because she wasn't quite together anymore, I mean in her head. I lost my father when I was eight years old.

"That's why my husband meant so much to me, you know. Ever since the death of my father, it was the first time I had a proper home, someone who really loved me. I was so unhappy before I met him. He was the first, the first one, I swear. And he was so gentle. In the evening he'd come into the kitchen where I was a maid and help me peel potatoes and wash dishes. When I took him one day to my room he was so happy, so grateful. I was scared but he was so gentle. He wanted to marry me right away, to take me away from the job. You're too good to be a maid, Nina, he'd say. When I protested he flew into a temper and yelled: I don't want no wife of mine to scrub floors for other people! That's how he was.

"My mother couldn't stand him. I don't know why. Maybe she thought he was a good-for-nothing because he'd changed jobs quite often when he didn't like where he was. He was proud. He didn't take garbage from nobody. But then she didn't like anyone no more. She was so spiteful. My God, she hated the whole world. She could never get over daddy's death, that he was murdered did something to her head, she was never the same after that. You sure I ain't boring you, Pat?. . .

"No, I don't mind talking about it as long as you want me to. I guess it feels kinda good to be talking about all of this. I remember the summer quite clearly. It was terrible. It was 1920, the height of the depression after the First World War when there was terrible need everywhere. I was eight years old then, the third of five children. My father always came home late in the evening. He was a foreman in a mine and always rode a bicycle home through the *Schrebergaerten* — you know, the little fenced off gardens people maintained to grow vegetables and things. They stretched for over a kilometer behind our apartment building. That evening it was hot and humid. I leaned out of the window because I couldn't sleep. Suddenly I heard a man screaming and a few minutes later two men came running out of the darkness waving their arms and then a whole lot of others followed them back into the gardens. My mother ran with them, along the path my father always took. A terrible fear had taken hold of her. I ran right behind her, quite beside myself too by this time from all the commotion. A crowd of people stood around someone lying there. His throat was cut so that I hardly recognized him. His clothes were soaked in blood.

"A bunch of men ran around with pitchforks and other tools they'd got from the gardens, stabbing around in the bushes, my mother running behind them screaming hysterically and me stumbling behind her blind with tears. And then suddenly there was a shrill scream. The man had hidden in a bush and someone had accidentally stabbed one of his eyes out with a pitchfork. He hung limp and whimpering between two men, blood and white stuff running down his cheek as he was led away. When she saw him mother threw herself on him and started beating up on him hysterically until they pulled her away.

"She could never get over it. Her whole character changed. For years she ran from judge to judge to get his sentence increased. No punishment was harsh enough for her. No kind word for anyone, only hatred and bitterness. Something just snapped in her.

"Of course it wasn't easy for her, with five children and a pension that was just barely enough to starve on. Still — I don't know — somehow I couldn't hate the man the way she did. Last year, right after the end of the war, they caught me with a pack of blackm'rket cigarettes and held me for a couple of days in prison and I found out that it was the same prison where he was being held. I asked permission to see him. What a sight! A small, pitiful man. Crying he clung to the bars of his cell with his one blind eye and haggard face and told me everything. I almost forgot that he'd murdered my father and only felt his terrible misery. And pity. A starving family had driven him to it. Afterwards he had felt such panic that he had thrown the money away. My father had just received his weekly pay check. It was never found either. Probably someone found it and put it in his own pocket.

"Oh God, I don't understand how all that can happen. He wasn't really a killer and they locked him up for life and my husband they sent out to kill and that was all right and he even received a medal for it and he never came back.

"You know, you become hard then and pretty soon you don't care about anything anymore. War makes you like that. Everything came on so fast too. You never had time to recover and become a human being again. You were hurried from one blow to the next so that you couldn't even stop and think and perhaps say No. It was a constant fight for survival and nothing beyond it, what lay behind and much less what lay ahead.

"Air raid after air raid. Sometimes the sirens went off before you even got back upstairs. Into the cellar, downstairs, upstairs, like a yo-yo, with a small suitcase in your hand and the children crying. And one day the building didn't stand above you anymore, everything in ruins, all your possessions gone. Christ, what do you care about anything then? In a train you sit with thousands of other evacuees, somewhere into the country they are taking you, you see the green landscape passing by but you curse it because all you can see in your brain are bomb craters and corpes. At night you feel sweating bodies all around you, you don't know where your own legs end, the kids lie somewhere else among strangers, and then a hand sneaks and touches you, you don't know where it comes from, to whom it belongs, you feel forgetfulness, your senses coming alive again, and you come together and separate, and then day dawns and the bodies break apart like a pitful of snakes, the people stretch and yawn and you don't even know exactly who it was. . .yes . .

"I'm happy you're here, *Lausbub*. I haven't felt that good with anyone for a long time. I'm so happy I met you."

Marijane G. Ricketts
Kensington, MD

Eye To Eye With Eliot

"Whatever we inherit from the fortunate
We have taken from the defeated. . ."

- From "Little Gidding (the fourth of the Four Quartets)"

Since your departure, the nations worldwide,
in stances peculiar, contradictions one-eyed,
entreaty at peace tables — tantamount to political tea.
The capital-rich, beyond per-capita castles,
the homeless stricken at their doors,
dine out according to their classes —
soup kitchens for the poor.

Century Twenty Star Wars, the ultimate deceit,
the chess game called no-nuclear retreat;
Cancer, non-curable Aids and guerrilla war
shrinking population to confused riproar.

Our panic not so much our own defense
as non-escape from one-world residence.

Superpowers nudge the pawns; terrorists retaliate;
our Latinate cousins mangled; the plague of cocaine;
the military python's stranglehold on economic gain
recoiling world opinion to its steely eye.

Death and re-birth the incontestable passport;
yes, one and the same
to television's rapid-fire cohorts.

Not yet is all well with our whimpering world,
arriving dead end where we began genetic whorl;
knowing only one Earth; one life-precious planet
suspended in space from the same shallow living room.

Outside, the horizon, the widening omen.

Stacey Sollfrey
Queens, NY

Coveralls

the substitute leg
dipped one more inch
of boneless skin
into the paint bucket
than the jowls of a hound dog
could've fitted through
the flares of bell bottomed pants
falling through dents
in cracks of day old cement
with the rindes of quarters
spinning in all directions
they ever wanted to

— ★ —

Circular Interuptus

the people's speech
says there's less
a chance of
majorities
screwing us over
than that one person
pointing out
all the directions
to the nearest welefare office
with all that prehistoric barefootness
being the only patches of animation
we could ever see

Karen Sexton-Stein
Laguna Hills, CA

Dear David

No one complains here
about scorching rays and skin cancer,
black clouds hovering in Hollywood streets
like hot dog vendors,
turbulent waves and faults
rocking me awake at dawn.

Like the bagladies in Venice
I, too, do not notice the sunsets
through the haze—I want to see it rise
over the Atlantic, lying in bed with my love
at Nags Head in July—Oh, those bungalows
with their mothballs, creaky boards
and windows that peel and open up and down
letting in the hot, summer rain.

There are no oaks to climb here
and I never hear any birds. The Pacific pelicans
are as unfriendly as the people—yes,
they are pretty from a distance,
graceful and scenic, but
under those handsome feathers
are fragile bones and flesh—
they have never learned the beauty of touch.

My heart aches to be touched, my mind—
a rotten cantaloupe—it is no wonder
people die of neglect here, hollowed inside out
from years of voluntary exhile. Skulls lie weathered
and cracked along the beaches of Santa Monica,
their emptiness scattered along the sand
with this year's storm sediment, waiting
to be washed away and pecked at
by tomorrow's pretty pelicans.

Ray Mizer
Greencastle, IN

Devotions

Some religionistic ones spin wheels
To send their piety aloft. Some go
And live alone in caves,
Far from the throng that maddens.
some lash themselves to bloody meat
To dramatize their penitence.
Devotionally, it's *chacun a son gout,*
And of tastes we say there's no disputing,
Though we do it endlessly.

One dissident pilgrim does his prayers
With a chisel and a mallet. His orisons rise
In tiny clouds of marble and limestone dust.
Here a mighty clout, there a whisper of touch.
Somewhere, he somehow knows,
In that inarticulate mass of matter
A fragment of truth and beauty lies
Confined and solitary, waiting,
Until he breaks the walls and bars
to set the spirit free.
A sure and steady hand is needed here.
This delicate surgery,
To free the pure essence from the dross,
Akin to that required by repairers of brains
Or separators of Siamese twins.
One gouge askew, one tap too much,
And all that waiting wonder
Dissolves in rubble and dust.

Maurice L. Dennett
Old Orchard Beach, ME

The Ace In The Hole

As certain as summer in years long past
Circus showbills would erupt and blaze
On walls and fences in cities and towns
And barns miles out on country roads
To announce a coming One Day Appearance
for Two Presentations of Exotic Spectacle
In sailcloth pavilions sun-whitened and taut
And a Street Parade at Eleven.

   You'll see no billowing domes today
   With masthead pennants gauging the wind,
   The troupers perform in stone coliseums
   And swap backlot gossip in coffee shops.

Yet somewhere a magnificent spirit must live
The pulse of a covenant kept by the breed,
A subtle spur in the jingling worksongs
They chanted on showgrounds across the nation
Moving the circus, pie wagon to big top
From town to town day by day.

   But clear to the mind as the lightning flash
   When thunder rushed the last show to finale
   Beginning the nightmare of pulldown time
   For a traveling tent show bedeviled by storm.

Then the cadence of workaday verse gave way
To trumpeting elephants still wearing spangles
Working the maze of blocks and tackle
Easing poles and tons of wet canvas to earth,
And teamster's curses and rattling harness
When lunging Clydesdales thrashed the traces
Of wagons miring in the softened field
While the show train waited on a rusted siding
A crosstown shuttle away.

They tramped a road uncluttered by milestones
Measuring their wealth in pocket change
But the prideful will of that roughcast legion
Could relay their world a hundred miles
Ready for fanfare with pennants flying
On another lot they'd reach at dawn,
Though rest was brief in the best of times
And bed was a flatcar hammering the rails.

The Screech Owl

High in the crown of an ancient oak
   a little grey owl slept deep and still
in its shaded berth drilled into the trunk
   by the rummaging beak of a vagrant flicker.

That nightfaring forager never knew
   when its citadel was uprooted today
and mauled into shreds by snarling engines
   stripping the tract for a shopping mall.

Nevermore shall I wait and watch at daybreak
   in a wooded haven flooding with birdsong
to log the time of the hunter's arrival
   home again from the stalking fields.

For the woodland lies in jackstraw mounds
   heaped leaf and bough by the clearing blades.
And mocked by a reek of ravaged earth
   is the balsamed mist we shared this morning.

ter To The Wake

He left at the beginning of the work week, and so it was
I sat in trenchcoat silence, found myself staring at a
Spanish sign for Winston (Lo Tiene Todo), momentarily
wondering what latitude the bus had droned into. Only
transitory, the bleached blonds said, dozing Romper Room
erect while spanish post-rush hour graffiti poured over
their lips. Thoughts cramped my ears, tilting with inertia.
My best friend's father is laid out tonight, had been all
day and I thought about last October. That was the last
time I can see his mouth filled with words; not accepting
messages over a cold phone. The bus hit the Kedzie underpass
and face bobbed up and down like empty lolling beer cans in
the water off Oak Street Beach. October 7. Sunday. He didn't
take it hard. I couldn't give Ray Sitowski a Cubs championship
and I can't give Dan his father back so what good is this
talent I have for being explicit? At 79th I spurted out the
doors like a broken blood vessel amid scattered Kit Kat
wrappers. I scrawl this with gloved hands as kids make figures
in the snow behind me. The bank clock says 6:19. 22°. 6:19.
My boots leave infinity-shaped prints in the snow as I walk
towards the funeral home

— ★ —

Don Wilson
Canton, CT

The Black Hills

Indians —
reservation
Indians — die, their holy
mountains covered with presidents'
faces.

Jason P. Smith
Nashville, TN

On Labor Day

The street cleaner
pressed his nose against midnight
and found he was the only one there

He was thinking about light
as he moved in and out
of the dark corners
of the city   sweeping darkness

Looking up at the staggering
buildings
he thought it would almost seem
like day
if all the lights came on   sweeping light

But then he didn't think
it would be so great
since
the hole in his shoe was getting
bigger
and everyone would see
the tobaco stains on his shirt   sweeping doubt

He was looking forward to
Labor Day
the next day in line
he could go visit his mother
or sit at home and play with the
dog
or spend the whole day
at the barber shop
that he knew not to be closed   sweeping hope

Remembering slowly
to look at his watch
he saw ten after

(more)

Jason P. Smith
con't.

one
and realised Labor Day
had started without him   sweeping alone

Picking up his broom
and walking home

Wayne Allen Sallee
Chicago, IL

Lines In Celebration of 21

Does one compose a phoenix
from pyres of past fetes?
At times, I find the ovenbird
misguided and melancholic,
and Eliot's Prufrock doomed,
stalking the tumid beach
of Nebraskan wheatfields,
Milwaukee suburbs,
and the grimoires
of assasins

This night a bellwether
for future ponderances
of desert meanderings,
rationalization fits
like an autumn glove
midst a celebration
of completion

A sedition against
youth

Jason P. Smith
Nashville, TN

I'm On My Way

My thoughts this morning
are only soft
and warm
like covering my hand
with sand on the beach

There are plenty of hard things
to think about
but they make me tired
and I get this wrinkle
in my brow
that is so tight

This morning the hallway
is filled
with a coolness
that can only
come on me as fall
When I step into the kitchen
the tile sends
that shiver through my foot

Dry leaves scrape across the driveway
I just know there's an army of them somewhere
needing to be raked
I saw pumpkins at a roadside stand yesturday
The urge to wear a sweater overtakes me
Brown comes out of hiding

But there are all those bills
and the car needs. . .
"Go hold someone's hand and take a walk"
I'm on my way
There's no need to yell

Andrea Potos
Oak Park, IL

Restoration

Here in the grandmotherly house
of my husband's childhood,
I am imbued
with a lost security
in the arched doorways and high ceilings
the lacey curtains hinting
at a leafy garden behind them,
the kitchen scents of warm apple pie
and biscuits.

I climb the attic steps
and lie down
on a wide feather bed,
its cool warm sheets
massaging my limbs and face.
Thirsty for a deep rest,
I drink sleep in the darkness
repairing the tensions
that repel me from life.

Steven G. Czarnetzki
Troy, MT

When The Coyotes Wail

When the coyotes wail
Snowshoe's soul cries out for life -
Worships it with flight.

William Rose
Brooklyn, NY

The Boy Who Could Do Magic

"Abracadabra."

A thick cloud of smoke rose from the shiny aluminum foil pie plate.

"Hocuspocusdominocus."

Another puff of smoke rose from the plate.

"Adarama."

A third, thicker cloud of smoke rose into the air.

Stanley looked at the plate in amazement and with considerable satisfaction. There was no doubt about it. The coin was no longer there.

Finally! This was *real* magic. No more clumsy conjuring tricks, no more hours of frustrating practice trying to manipulate cards that were larger than his hands. From now on Stanley would be able to make things go his way. This wasn't make-believe magic; it was the real thing.

Stanley savored this moment of triumph. No more being pushed around by his family, no more bullying by Allen Stoner. If something or someone made Stanley unhappy he would simply make that something or someone go away.

Stanley had yearned for real magic for years. It wasn't easy being a kid, but being an only child in a household run by women resembled life in a concentration camp, as far as Stanley was concerned. It was "Do this, Stanley," "Don't do that, Stanley," "Have you done your homework, Stanley," "How can you get your clothes so filthy, Stanley," all day long. The idea of getting rid of one of the overpowering matriarchs with a mere snap of the fingers was an extremely attractive one to a lonely nine year old.

Not to speak of his teachers, those other adult tyrants in his life. Mr. Samuelson, his history teacher, wasn't so bad. He showed interesting films from time to time and let them get into some real discussions in class. Stanley wouldn't make him disappear. But Mrs. Harkins, his math teacher, was a definite candidate for the occult arts. The utter torture of fractions and factoring and problems in which one train leaves point A going fifteen miles per hour and another train leaves point B going thirteen miles per hour, and you have to figure out at which point. . .enough! The brain boggles at such questions, and Stanley felt not the slightest compunction for anyone who would torment young children in that way.

And then there was Allen Stoner. Stanley as yet had encountered no punishment sufficiently horrendous for Allen Stoner. Mere disappearance seemed too kind a fate for such a monster. When Stanley's family had moved from Indiana to Arkansas, it had been Allen Stoner who had pinned Stanley to the ground in front of their schoolmates and forced him to admit he was a damned yankee. Stanley had yielded because Allen Stoner was built like a Sherman tank and Allen's father had committed the crime against humanity of teaching his son to box. Furthermore, when Stanley looked up at the faces looking down on him as he lay there with his nose bleeding all over his new shirt, he saw that they were totally devoid of pity. No, the only thing to do under the circumstances was to eat crow, but Stanley retained the most utter hatred for Allen Stoner. He didn't want a fast punishment for his adversary. Only roasting over a low flame or impaling on a sharp stake or—most awful of all!—an eternity of solving Mrs. Harkins' math problems, were tortures adequate for such evil. No, making him disappear into the great unknown was much too easy for Allen Stoner.

Magic had always appealed to Stanley as a weapon against more powerful adversaries. He had first encountered it in the Oz books and had been delighted with the way girls like Glinda and Ozma could defeat powerful enemies with their mysterious powers. And then there was the Wizard of Oz. When he read about the Wizard's little black bag he quickly fashioned one for himself, emptying his marbles out of their black leather pouch and filling it with a collection of magic powders, because any magic worthy of the name seemed to involve the burning of some kind of powder. The powders were actually face powder, talcum powder, bicarbonate of soda and various chemicals from his Gilbert Chemistry Set, but that couldn't be helped. It was all he had. Besides, he knew the really important part was to know the proper incantations.

This problem had him stumped until he discovered an anonymous work in the local library entitled *Complete Book of the Occult and Fortune Telling*. The volume was a dusty one hidden in a far corner of the stacks, a place Stanley was only allowed to enter because he sometimes helped the librarian, Mr. Birnbaum, dust the books and move them from one place to another. In return, Mr. Birnbaum allowed Stanley the privilege of browsing in the stacks to his heart's content. Stanley loved books. They were a great consolation in the midst of an otherwise depressing world, and when he found this particular book he realized immediately that he had come upon an incredible treasure.

Stanley hid the book under his jacket because he suspected that Mr. Birnbaum might not think it appropriate reading for a young boy. Mr. Birnbaum kept a number of books by authors of whom he disapproved—Kurt Vonnegut, D. H. Lawrence, Vladimir Nabokov, etc.— off the shelves and this one had certainly not been accesible to the general public hidden away in that corner. When Stanley got home he immediately locked the book in the locker at the foot of his bed since he was also certain his family would not approve of it. He had heard his mother tell his aunt once that she thought it was bad for him to read the Oz books "because the boy lives in a fantasy world and it's just not healthy for him," so he knew a book about the occult would hardly be considered wholesome entertainment. He really couldn't understand why they were so concerned about what he read since most of his friends didn't read anything at all and their parents were constantly trying to cut down on their TV viewing time, while Stanley had the greatest contempt for the boob tube. He had no time for it, between his homework and his own reading. He liked to read, to lose himself in a book for hours on end, and now that reading was becoming a clandestine activity it was even more appealing.

The book was fascinating. Stanley soon learned the difference between High Magic and Low Magic, and the various categories of the latter, which was what interested him most: amulets and talismans, spells, pacts, pentacles, sorcery, curses, etc. There was a certain lack of detail, but, since Stanley had no way in a small town of obtaining conjuring books mentioned by the author (the *Grimoire of Pope Honorius,* the *Grimorium Verum,* the *Clavicle of Solomon,* the *Enchiridion* and others with equally tantalizing titles), he supplemented the few hints he encountered scattered here and there throughout the book with his own imagination.

His first experiments were complete flops. He burned powders and muttered encantations and waved his hands in the air and absolutely nothing happened. But one day, while he was trying to make a coin disappear, he struck pay dirt. Whether he had hit on the proper combination of words or—more probably—whether he had achieved the proper concentration of mental energy necessary to achieve the "vibratory condition" that, according to the book, enables the sorcerer to act, the fact is that the coin disappeared, and Stanley wasn't one to quarrel with success.

His next step was to try out his newfound powers on living things. He was afraid at first that it might just work on inanimate objects, like coins and stones, but would have no effect on flesh and blood. But no, first the Johnson's poodle and then Mrs. Allison's cat vanished as completely as the coin had. He didn't know if they were disappearing into another dimension or being dissolved into their constituent atoms, and he cared less; the important thing was that they were gone. Stanley wasn't interested in metaphysical theory; the only thing that concerned him was the practical application of his art.

Then came the fatal day when Allen Stoner decided that he had left Stanley in peace for too long. It was in gym, and the coach had let Allen and Ralph Jones put on boxing gloves for a few rounds. Allen hated Ralph, a quiet, studious boy, but one who had committed the grievous sin—in Allen's eyes—of being black. Allen made Ralph's life miserable in as many ways as he could, and Ralph had finally gotten tired of it and invited Allen to a few rounds in the ring. Allen was delighted because he considered himself an invincible boxer, but it turned out that Ralph was no slouch himself and Allen soon found himself flat on his back with Ralph Jones looking down at him with a satisfied smile on his face.

Stanley was among the spectators who were deriving great pleasure from seeing Allen get his comeuppance. Allen pulled himself to his feet and glared at his classmates.

"All right, which one of you gutless heroes wants to put on the gloves with me?" he demanded. Then he saw Stanley. "How about you, Fisher?" he sneered. "Want to go a few rounds, or haven't you got the balls? Scared, little man?"

Stanley definitely didn't want to box with Allen but he could hardly turn down such an insulting challenge, especially since it had been delivered in front of all the others. So with a sick feeling in his stomach he let someone lace the gloves on his hands and then step- ped into the ring.

The rest was something that Stanley didn't want to remember, and whenever he did his face burned with shame. He hadn't been able to put a glove on Allen even though he'd tried, oh, how he'd tried to hit that grinning, contempuous face. But Allen blocked his clumsy swings with ease and knocked Stanley all over the ring until he felt that he had regained some of the status he'd lost in the bout with Ralph Jones. Stanley hadn't been hurt very much physically—he didn't even have a black eye—but the spiritual bat- tering had been brutal. Stanley had never felt so humilliated in his life, and he was sick with rage. He didn't hear a word his teachers said the rest of the day, and he had the feeling everyone was look- ing at him and snickering behind his back.

When he got home after school he went straight to his room and took his paraphernalia out of the foot locker. He placed the pie plate on his desk and sprinkled three mounds of powder on it. He had to be careful because he was running low and he wasn't sure what ingredients had gone into the concoction, or what the propor- tions had been. But there was enough for what he wanted to do now, and he chuckled with savage glee as he made his preparations.

Then he opened the previous year's school yearbook, circled Allen Stoner's face with a black marker, and began to concentrate on it. He'd made many things disappear, but this was the first time he'd tried to make a person disappear. It was also the first time he'd done it with such active malice. Even Mrs. Allison's cat, a spoiled feline that he threw stones at whenever no one was looking, hadn't aroused such hatred as Allen Stoner's face. He had regarded the cat as the object of an experiment, but now he wanted revenge. He felt as though he had never hated anyone with such a consuming passion as he did the grinning face in the photograph.

"Abracadabra," he said. *Go, damn you.* Puff! One of the mounds of powder ignited spontaneously and released a thick cloud of acrid smoke.

"Hocuspocusdominocus." *Disappear, you bastard.* Puff! A

second mound of powder ignited. The room was now hazy with smoke.

"Adarama," Stanley said, and the last mound of powder belched a huge cloud of smoke into the air.

Stanley's grandmother, who was walking down the hall at that moment, saw the smoke seeping out from under the door and thought the house was on fire. She yanked open the door and, stumbling and coughing through the foul-smelling smog, opened the window.

In a moment the smoke cleared and she was able to see the pie plate with burn marks scarring its shiny surface on Stanley's desk, but otherwise the room was empty. Then she noticed that a book was lying open on the desk. She looked closer and saw that it was a school yearbook and that Allen Stoner's photograph had been circled in black ink. Except that where the photograph had been there was now just a blank space on the page.

The police classified the double disappearance as a case of two runaways and promptly forgot about it. But Stanley's grandmother, who had seen the smoke in the room and examined the contents of his foot locker, knew perfectly well what those pleading voices were she heard in the night. Shortly thereafter the family committed her to the state mental hospital where she was diagnosed as a hopeless schizophrenic and held under heavy sedation until her death six months later. As for the boys, they were never seen again.

Corky Miller
New Hope, PA

An 8th Grade Class Portrait

Girls, in their round-collar blouses, wool
A-line skirts, colored knee socks that matched
100% virgin wool cardigan sweaters, regulation Bass
Weejun loafers-the ones with the fringed flap being the
most desirable,
made fun of the women who shopped in Bonwit Teller or
Wanamakers. Bleached-blond hairdos
in tight black torredor pants and
regulation pointed black flats-not Capezios,
were the cause of many a giggle and pointed finger,
and accents "Dahlink, don't you think these fuschia
slacks are beautyful?" while mouths gave new meaning to the
art of cracking gum. My friends

would laugh and say "oh, they're so Jewish", look at
me, quickly adding that I wasn't, I didn't even look
It.
Relief, oh thank God, I pass.
My imitations were the best in my group, I
was always a clever actress. Until

Mrs. Miller, the sloppily dressed history teacher
decided that anti-semitism was an issue
in my liberal Quaker school.
I didn't want to talk to her, but I liked her. She
was different,
like me. "What are your experiences here with
anti-semitism?" her voice was soft and warm.
The entertainer was mute, my betrayal complete.
When I could no longer look at her
I walked out.

Joe Lackey
Wichita Falls, TX

Allure In A Yellow Light

The colors exploded
in the darkness of the midnight
sky—orange and blue,
red and green shot streaks
through the Milky Way
and beyond. The traveler
gaped at her — she ran
across the field, bounding
above the rocks, above
the cactus, running on
air, a vision of pure
beauty, beyond perfection,
beyond the beyond,
and yet present, an entrancing
presence. He lifted
an arm a few inches—it fell
back to his side.
Surrounded by the radiance
of a soft yellow light,
she bounded gracefully
toward the borders of ineffability.
Her white gown swirled
and flowed as she surged
through the night. He tried
to cry out, but could not—his
eyes swam from their feast
on beauty. The only sound
he could hear in the stillness
of the desert came from the sudden
whinny of a horse somewhere
in the distance. The traveler
began to weep as she flowed
into the edge of the night—
muffled hoofbeats could be heard,
and then

Mary Ann Henn
St. Joseph, MN

Witches' Brew

(Not dedicated to God)

Your chains enforce an emotional
slavery. Away from you, I recognize
wicked air thick with witchcraft
the boiling bubbling bones
the yellow scum along
             the edges of your pot.
I inhale a witches' brew
recall the naked dance
among the snagging trees.
Who
    drank my blood?
Who
    sang my incantations?
Who
    tore my heart
    with cruel manipulations?
You?
    You twisted my mind
    but I never knew.
Your sorcerer of sorts—
    I loved you.

Carmen M. Pursifull
Champaign, IL

Death Is A Spaceship 6X6

Cross beams of light hold.
Space is six feet by six feet.
This is the area of her existence
sometimes undulating from the rigid square.

She pokes a finger at the barrier
finding a hole untethered by beam-bars.
     The finger explores
     fondles the opening
     working it larger.

She braves burns pin-prickling nerves
rides a gusty wind to unknown destinations.

The stars are alien debris her
     threaten to nova
as she floats through time.
She is repulsed attracted
joined distracted dislodged
     by boulders flying by.
Time mammoths her till she collapses
exploding into decibles too high to hear.

Gas clouds of light hold.
Space is unlimited and she is lost
cooling to a substance new
subjugated to the whole around her
subjugated to the whole within her.

Kay Weems
Artemas, PA

Summer In The City

Day in, day out everthing's the same -
morning deliveries to Jewish deli,
smell of barrel pickles and kosher,
sign in window says .15 and
iceman's wagon rolls to a stop.
I run to catch flying chips. . .
feel coolness as he passes by.
Mrs. Goldman wants her lights turned on
and holds me up to reach the chain;
giving an orange for my reward.
The Arab sings his familiar song
and old women hurry for newspaper bundles.
Clippity clop, clippity clop -
another wagon rolls over the cobblestones -
and covering eyes for my familiar game
I say, "This one will be a white horse."
An endless stream of trucks and wagons roll by.
"Where do they come from, where do they go?"
I drag a stick along cracks in sidewalk
watching ants run helter skelter.
Two old men sit under a tree,
captivated by board between their knees.
"I got you this time, Jake. King me,"
and he slaps his leg and grins.
Icecream cone brings me back to more
pressing problem, as cool, sticky substance
runs down my arm. . .I
suck its juices from the bottom.
Leaning back on elbow I wait. . .
savoring coolness of marble steps
during hot city summer.

Dori Anne Steele
Silver Spring, MD

New Patterns

A limb outstretched -
grows towards a bank
that it cannot feel yet.

A natural bridge
bending and arching like
the curve of the spine
-that sinuous cord of
nerves and impulses-

There's always a compromise
in moving on/a weighing
of what you have —
against what you desire.

There is pain in new growth -
the tender breaking-through
of green shoots - and that
period of vulnerability.

You cannot go back —
you find the places changed, and
your presence not as essential -
as you had always imagined.

Lean forward - reach -
grasp for a strong-hold
where you can plant roots -
and blossom with exotic flowers.

Even the bark of your flesh
will bear new patterns. . .

Kim J. Kennedy
Coos Bay, OR

Down To The Beach

I'll go down to the sea now,
watch the waves grow and shrink,
come and go, deliver and take away
as I walk and bend and kneel
barely disturbing the age old sand,
my confusion not yet complete.

Will you miss me this time?
Don't give it a second thought, babe,
I'll bury my dreams in the sand,
erect a cross with Jesus the crucified,
scatter a pound of emotional ashes,
then settle down to die.

The death squad will slowly circle
their strong wings still, heavy
in the stiffling midday mist of life.
I see in those brown deer eyes
a certain knowledge and fear.
I won't be here at the end of the search.

Kim J. Kennedy
Coos Bay, OR

Dream Sequence

The stuff dreams are made of
floats down cheeks moist with tears,
the cats don't even laugh
but lick up the salty moisture
turning dingy skin into aromatic roses.

You amble powerfully through my nights;
the leopard of bruised, weary pursuits
guzzling the hot blood of my heart,
chewing intently the secret of my horror,
slowly swallowing the bits of my panic.

Muses don't comfort me in my dreams.
I sleep hanging on a coat rack
waiting for the harvest moon
to take you away to fly in hell,
to-take-you-away. No nightmares.

Michael Fitzgerald
Winchester, VA

Report To Basho

The Twentieth Century Thus Far

An eagle landed on the moon,
a black slave
became Senator of
the most powerful nation on earth,
darkness became light,
and a peasant
became Czar of Russia.

Ann Klein Cooper
Deer Park, NY

It's Off Her Chest

Importance of the Breast: Stacked; Petted; and Sex-ploited

The beauty of the human female has always depended upon her bustline. If liberally endowed and seductively shaped, her sexual appeal would know no bounds. When cheated by nature and flat-chested, she would have to compensate with other virtues (talent, intelligence and perhaps a "pretty face.")

Kathy Huston was one of the fortunate of her gender, being amply full-figured. However, she detested using this advantage to in any way enhance her sexuality and she brought this problem before her psychiatrist, in one of their more candid sessions. She reflected on her mother's tragic illness, which erupted in that area, and her own fears and anxieties regarding marital lust.

"Do you like it when your husband feels your breasts?" unknowingly Dr. Conroy had touched a sensitive area.

"He doesn't anymore," Kathy sat with her legs primly crossed in Conroy's closet sized office on the third floor.

"Why is that?" Conroy continued the embarrassing line of questioning.

"Because I've asked him not to," Kathy remained composed.

"You must have a good reason for keeping him from enjoying this common form of marital pleasure. Would you care to tell me what it is?"

"It's a painful story," Kathy became flustered, "I'd rather not discuss it."

"I'm here as your psychotherapist to listen to all your painful stories, so you might as well start with this one."

"About a year ago my mother lost her right breast to cancer; she had a mastectomy. It was disfiguring and frightening for her and traumatic for the whole family."

"Cancer is never pleasant," commented Conroy.

"Somehow, I always remembered the times I'd seen my father fondle my mother's breasts. He would pinch and squeeze them and she'd start to laugh; they were very affectionate."

"Do you blame your father for your mother's breast cancer?" Conroy asked quietly.

"No, but I started to believe that the act of petting might be related to the cause of cancer, Jim said I was crazy.''

"Is Jim gentle when he caresses you there?''

"Frequently, when I do let him, he gets carried away and then I'll be left with bruises, even a few black and blue marks. He likes to bite me, also.''

"But now he does nothing? Is he satisfied with that?''

"No, but that's the way it has to be.''

"You are making a big mistake denying him, Mrs. Huston, because there are few things a man enjoys more than having his hands on a good pair. I can assure you that medically your fears are unfounded. There is no connection between manipulation and malignancy. If there were most of the women in the world would be dying of breast cancer." He helped her out of her chair and opened the office door.

The late model Buick Sedan sped along the New Jersey Turnpike heading for New York City. The driver reached a hand over to give a comforting pat to the woman beside him. She had been crying continuously since they left Baltimore.

"She looks so awful, Arty. I've never seen Kathy look so bad before. The way she walks and dresses and her beautiful hair was such a mess.''

"Remember Gert, they have no mirrors there.''

"That place, Arty, that dreadful depressing institution. Why won't Jim take her out of there? Four months is long enough.''

"You know he won't because he's listening to her doctor.''

"What kind of man is that doctor, anyway? Did you know what he told Jim? To divorce Kathy. He thinks she's hopeless and will be in there for years. What can he know of life, he's so young himself.''

"Arty, we'll lose our grandchildren. Jimmy, Kim and that beautiful baby, God love him,'' she wept even more. Her voice was thick with emotion,'' Arty, what can we do?''

"I've investigated the doctor, for starters. He's just a smart-ass rich kid from Jersey City.''

"What's he got against our Kathy?''

"Maybe the question is what's he got going for her. He's a pretty fast bachelor I understand.''

Mrs. Gertrude Kurry continued to sob quietly.

"Don't worry Gert, I'm going to do everything legally possible to get Kathy out of that hell hole; and if that doesn't work we'll try something not so legal.

Do you want anything to eat Gert? I think I'm going to pull in at the next rest stop; we need gas."

At one time, she had felt that losing her breast to cancer was the worst blow life could deal her. Gertrude Kurry had adjusted to that tragedy but now she seemed to be losing her only daughter and the grandchildren, as well. She could picture nothing except a sudden painful death being as miserable as her current circumstance!!

The six o'clock nightly news broadcast blared from the old T.V. console in the Huston living room. The three small children still mesmerized from a cartoon show that they had watched for the previous hour, continued to listen as the newscaster related the up-to-the-minute news. His voice droned on in the familiar staccato rhythm barely pausing for a breath, "A destructive fire raged through the Pediatric Hospital at the University Medical Center downtown earlier today. Miraculously, all the children were safely evacuated due to the heroic efforts of the medical staff and the local firefighters. Several adult patients in the adjoining Psychiatric Hospital were not so fortunate and had to be treated for burns and smoke inhalation. Sources believe the fire started spontaneously in the linen closet on the fourth floor of the children's facility."

"Daddy, isn't the University Medical Center the hospital where Mommy is?" Jimmy, Jr. had become alarmed by the news. He frequently thought about his absent mother.

"No need to worry Jimmy, as soon as I heard the bulletin about the fire on the car radio I drove to the University Medical Center. They assured me your mother is fine and was completely unharmed in the fire. I couldn't see her because it wasn't visiting hours at that time but I'll be seeing her tomorrow. She's fine son don't worry about it another minute. Let's go eat dinner now."

Kathy was far from feeling fine next visiting day. She was bordering on hysteria, "Do you have any idea, Jim Huston, how terrifying it is to be trapped inside a burning building with no way out because there are bars on all the windows and every exit is locked? The thick smoke was seeping in through the windows and under the doors almost suffocating us and still no one would let us out. The heat became so intense I thought I would be cooked alive. James, a very simple minded patient, got near the flames and was badly burned. They had to transfer him to the burn unit. He may not live! The doors were there but we couldn't walk out of them to safety we had to stand in his hell hole and sweat like desperate criminals. I want you to take me out of this fire trap of a prison. If you won't then be prepared to live without me because I will divorce you as soon as I get out." With those searing words, Kathy had made her ultimate threat.

The Kurrys were just pulling into their Long Island driveway after the long, depressing trip when the news of the hospital fire was announced as a "special bulletin," on network news. "We must remove our Kathy from that horrid place," Gert screamed in despair. "Nothing else matters anymore." agreed her fatigued husband. "Damn Jim, anyway!" Art mumbled under his sour breath.

— ★ —

Helen Engelhardt
Brooklyn, NY

This Season

Love is all
we are able to give one another
this season. Not hope, exactly.
Certainly not certainty.
Continuity is spidersilk thin
and as tenacious.
It may in time be torn
beyond repair.
Now it leads us through
the maze of our days
into spun air.

Howard Bernstein
Colts Neck, NJ

The Twelfth House

Sunset let an artery for us while
We glisten with the leaf,
With the edge of threadbare park,
With the narrowing of twilight
Spilling darkness into dark.
Are we but the educated clever on the climb
Informed of near and far,
Taking soundings of the shoals,
Steering course by neon star?
What is there that touched the heart?
Did we not march for Sharpeville,
But were we bruised by others' wounds?
All things we do are done in fits and starts.
This summer it is the Zodiac.
She reads aloud,
"'The Twelfth House is of the hidden enemy, our own undoing.'"
"Yes, he said, "the house of dread that rises with us
From our bed and shaves in our looking glass."
He laughs, she laughs, we laugh.
Are we only of the present tense weary of the climb?
No one guessed, we temporized
And mostly missed the mark
As sundown bled darkness into dark.

Seymour Hakim
APO, NY

Eleusinian Caves

Dante knew
the Eleusinian Caves,
the mysteries
whose solution he sought
wandering
between death
and hope. . .
shore and caverns
with the pebbles
and the mustard seed,
the search for resurrection.

He didn't write of Kore,
mention Persephone
or Demeter
but he knew
their ancient lands
and the legends,
had heard their songs
in Tuscany,
studied
the cult of fire,
the sacrifices of purification
Dante chose Beatrice-
the light of beatitude-
for the search,
to persue the way,
caverns and caravans
flaming rivers
and boiling lands,
parched breath
and the silence of death,
he went to wander
the footsteps of Orpheus
in search of Eurydice.

There had been
the music
of the lyre-claimed
to calm the ranging beasts,
echoes in caverns
chaos
primeval darkness-black
Charon's dogs. . .
the medieval magician's call
the tempest's mark
and the toll of time.
Dante knew
that the ascension
must be more,
must go beyond
the ancient forest's path,
must suprpass
the tidal waves,
the deep green waters-Lethe-
the washing of shores,
the daemons waiting
on the Elysian Fields.

He must ascend
the narrow passageways
from cave to cave-
masked with terrors,
man's new born knowledge
and growing dread,
he must ascend
beyond the harmony
of the deceiving silence
of Prospero's hymns
and sleight of waving hand.

Dante's bargain
would be for more-
between self and self

(more)

Seymour Hakim
con't.

and unknown force
he'd bear the weight
of time,
pebbles and mustard seeds
and anxieties toll;
his search:
the purification of the spirit
the calming of the soul.

Mary Ann Henn
St. Joseph, MN

There It Is Again

"Tell me
about the contemplative life,"
he said and I knew
he had visions of holy penguins
walking a tunnel to chapel
eyes guarded hands folded
an organ playing in the background
This black and white bird would bow
and genuflect humbly kneel
in her pew in direct contact
with saints angels and God
Himself unaware of anything
going on around her
Partly he was curious and I can
understand that but please
don't put a halo where it
      doesn't belong

Joyce S. Mettelman
New Hartford, NY

Prescience

What was that special instinct all those years ago,
That prescience that made me turn to you?
Drawn to you, magnetized, loving and fearing your touch,
Not understanding all those joyous, troubled nights and days.
It wasn't in the books or ads at all:
The Cinderella-story of a marriage did not include that sort of
                                                    happening.
And so I fought love, lost you, found and refound understanding,
Down the circling staircase of the years —
And, inexplicably, won.
Tonight, riding with the moon above my shoulder,
I laugh at science, feel the awesome power of instinct.
See that moon, I think,
Blanketed in mist at first, then clearly outlined —
A bright, luminous half-pie-in-the-sky.
You scientists may have plumbed the moon's cold spaces,
Walked her dust, carved chunks of boulder, named her places.
But what do you really know of her?
She is, after all, the moon of mystery, of instinct,
Unknown.
Pre-science.
Fathomless as love, still symbolizing love.
Prescient, she guides me homeward:
Our instincts all at last fulfilled.

Eddena Christian
El Monte, CA

Fun House

Broken images
Sparkling shards of glass
Parting and joining
Creating pictures
Then destroying them
Like thoughts in a life
Unity is more of a distortion
Than Separation

— ★ —

Carmen M. Pursifull
Champaign, IL

The System Of Roots

the mindscape
likens to a swamp
of tentacles
entrenched in thought
some spread a cancer
an underskin rebellion
from years arrested
in shrouded screams
they swell from swollen roots
decay/loosen the deluge
of sedentary sentiment
and acid floods the eyes

          freed

mind finds itself again
among the ruins.

Margaret Rosenborg
NY, NY

Flower Petal

There was
A white form
With petals
Like a flower
Laying on
A pale red sea
Held like a nest
On the head
Of a giant black bird
And
An old man was playing
Sweet jazz on his violin
With a young drummer
Beating his drum
With his soul
The white form
Became
A dancing figure
Wearing
White petaled dress
Whirling and tapping
To a medley
Of melodious songs
When
Suddenly the pale
Pink water parted
And
A great voice sounded
Almost with
A deep calling moan
The figure heard
A song
And danced down
The pathway
As the violin played
And drums beat
'Going Home.'

Michael Fitzgerald
Winchester, VA

Shenandoah River Poem

The breeze of a coming autumn,
from the waning heat of August,
even then, comes cool over the hills
of the Shenandoah Valley.
The longing for the road dies down
in the shelter of the Blue Ridge,
and notice is placed with my friends
that this is home enough.
The common birds, jay, robin,
and the cardinal come and go in town
and the eagle and the tanager
fly the hills. A motion of itself,
mortal and beautiful, the river
runs here to make the song of spring
laugh in advance, and the cost of winter
becomes endurable, an invitation
to warmth. I take me to my friends' cabins
for a night of whispers by the river,
to seek the perfect thing it is.

Thomas Laird
West Peoria, IL

Chronicle

Morning

I have to be up at dawn, she says.

There might be some trouble at the school and we're supposed to get there before the rest of the kids do.

She's just trying to make it easier for me to get back to *normal*, she keeps on saying. I understand her, I think. She doesn't need to draw me any pictures.

Dad leaves for work at 5:30. He works by the Wisconsin border—construction. Things have been going better for him since the weather's been so dry. Every day is a work day, lately, for him. And I know he'd rather be out of the house than be around while all this has been happening. He's never backed off or anything—I don't mean he'd like to run out on Mom and me. It's just that the last time a photographer showed up at school, Dad got pissed and threw a fist into his lens. The lens and camera popped back into the photographer's face, and Mom said we almost had a lawsuit on our hands. Until Dad paid for a new camera.

But I think he would rather be at work—pounding nails, watching walls go up, pouring concrete—anything. I know *I'd* be relieved to get out of here before dawn breaks, these days.

Mom leaves for her secretary job at 8:00, so she has plenty of time to drive me to school. She's been taking me a half hour before the playground officially opens, ever since the word got out—

I had the dream again last night. Same dream as always. It's a vampire movie in my head, of course. The creature's a man, and he comes after me, like vampires do in the movies—But when he wraps his arms around me, and just when I think I'm going to see those two blood-dripping fangs, out pops two needles. They pop right out of his gums as soon as he opens his mouth *wide*.

I know what the dream means. I don't need a shrink to explain them to me.

All my family talks about it as if it's one big tragedy. One huge mistake somebody made. It was supposed to be just a blood transfusion and I wind up the way I am, now. There's the lawsuit against the hospital, and I suppose we've got a good chance of winning some money from them—

But who cares? It's not like the money'll pay for my college education, like my Dad says. And when he said it in front of me, he colored kind of quick and then he embarrassed me in front of Mom by hugging me, long and hard. I'm getting too old to be hugged by him. I just thank God he didn't do that in front of—

I was going to say in front of *my friends*, but since they've all gone away, I guess I don't have to worry about them being an audience to my father being carried away.

I did my crying and I'm done with it. My mom still cries—usually she tries to lock herself in her bedroom or in the john so I won't hear her—but it doesn't happen as often anymore.

We went to the hospital for counseling, but the psychiatrist didn't help us out very much. It just seems like you can weep over something for just so long, and then you get numb. My Mom hasn't arrived at numb, yet, but I think I'm there. I think I'm already there.

I'm not able to watch much television in the mornings any longer. We have to leave too early, and most of the daybreak stuff is a little childish, I think. The *Count Duckulas* and all that little guy stuff. I still get a laugh out of *The Brady Bunch* and *Andy Griffith,* but I've seen them all too many times to be interested in turning on the tube before we leave for school.

"You ready, Jay?" Mom asks.

I show her my lunch sack—I've developed the habit of making my own lunch in spite of her bitching about how much she loves to make it for me.

I could barely hear her because I'm still plugged into my Walkman—Listening to Van Halen's new cuts. I can't hack the radio in the morning because they mostly play little guy tunes—You know, Pebbles and Belinda Carlisle and all those other ten year olds' heartthrobs. I think I passed Madonna and all that in sixth grade, last year. Heavy metal is where I'm at, at the moment. Even those old dudes—Led Zeppelin—beat the hell out of all that candy-assed rock for all those *pre-pubies.*

So I got a disease. The sun still comes up. Every day. Sure, sometimes I feel sick and I stay home from school, but the sickness passes pretty fast, and I'm usually only out one day—

Now that they can't keep me out permanently.

It took three months of lawyers and judges to get me back in, the time after the principal met Mom and me out in front of the school's steps. Naturally all the TV guys and the news guys were there. It scared me a little--But not as much as my vampire dream does. The nightmare with the monster with the hypo-needle fangs, I mean.

But now I go to school, and sometimes I pay attention in class and sometimes I don't give a shit what *anyone's* saying, all day long. Sometimes I just listen because the day drags by too slowly if I *don't.* So I guess I'm learning stuff whether I feel like it or not.

Some of my teachers are sympathetic. They go out of their way to make me feel like I'm still part of everything. But we all know it's a big joke. A farce, you know. I'm not stupid, even though I was never an acer student. I know when I'm being what they call 'patronized'. There are kids and adults who are scared shitless I'll give them what I've got, and there are other people at school who just don't want to be around me because they think I'm the product of some junkie and his junkie wife. They know my story by now. They *know* it was the fault of that hospital. But some people think what they want to think, so it's all *our* faults that I'm around to re-mind them of something real unpleasant. It's like I'm that 'Elephant Man'—except that I'm not ugly like he was.

Maybe the ugly is just on my insides, they think. Maybe that's good enough for them to stay the hell away from me. I don't really know what they think because I'm damned if I'll ask them what's going on inside their fevery little skulls.

"Are you *ready, Jay!*" she shouts.

I turn off my music, take off the headphones, and we're out the door.

Noon

No photographers, today. I'm old news by now. I'm sort of *tolerated*, you might say. They don't come any closer than they have to, but they at least leave me alone.

There was some name-calling when I first came back to school, but some of those patronizing teachers put a stop to it.

Maybe I'm giving those teachers too much the bad review, here, but it's hard for me to know who to trust. I trust my mother and father, but that's as far as it goes. There are only the three of us in the family, and all Mom's and Dad's family are on the East Coast, a thousand miles away. And I don't think they're all fired up about getting on a jet and coming here to comfort us in our time of need.

I look back at the front of the classroom. It's fourth hour. Social studies. We're doing the colonial period. Which is very boring, to say the least. The teacher—Mrs. Rolinski—is not the problem. It just seems like government and all that taxation without representation stuff is very *dead weight*. I *know* it's the history of our country and I know what a special place this country's supposed to be, but—

Then she starts talking about how we were "*ostracized*" by the Brits when we started raising hell over here and my ears zoom in on her words. She goes on about how one of the biggest things that marks the U.S. is that we did all that fighting and dying for one big reason: *The right to be different*. Man, that really strikes a hefty bass note inside my chest—for some reason I'm not real sure about. But after she says that business about the right to be different, I'm following her every word. Right up until the bell rings.

Then the girl across the aisle from me pops her gum. But she doesn't smile back at me when I shoot her some grins.

The dumb cooz.

I eat my lunch by myself, off in a corner of the cafeteria. No one had to tell me to sit off by myself, but I knew enough to do it on my own. I like to eat by myself, anyway. There's nothing stupider looking than feeding your face. I even have to look away when my mother and father get a little string of juice flowing down to their chins. It almost makes me want to gag, but I've learned to watch my plate, when I'm here at school and when I'm home at the dinnertable.

I usually leave half of my lunch in the bag, lately. Only thing that tastes good is sweets. So I dump the sandwich I made for myself—Mom insists I eat meat and bread or cheese and bread—and I eat Twinkies or Ho-Ho's or whatever goo my mother buys for the lunches. I drink a can of Coke or Pepsi along with them because I can't get milk down, anymore.

It's raining today, and that's the worst time for me. When it's clear, I can go out into our little campus and sit by myself till it's time to go to the next class. But when they keep us indoors, it seems like a very long forty-five minute period.

There are people who would talk to me, I'm sure. There are a couple do-gooders in every school, I bet. This place is no different. But the fact is I've run out of stuff to say to people and I think they've run out of little nothings to share with me. So I'll save us both the trouble.

Thank Christ the bell rings and I'm off to Science. Today we're talking about the Voyager and how we're going to get back into space after that bad thing that happened a couple of years back.

I remember that bad thing. I saw it on TV, like most everybody else.

It happened before I went to the hospital. It was for a simple, day-in, day-out, run-of-the-mill operation. I had my appendix taken out. I don't really remember the transfusion.

The operation was a success. It went perfectly. My stomach ache just disappeared.

Evening

Van Halen is on my plugged-in, personal jukebox again. The tune is "Black and Blue". I'd really like to see them when they come into town next summer, but I don't plan on anything, of course. My Mom keeps talking about high school and college. Instead of making her feel bad I just tell her I want to join the Air

Force and fly jets like Tom Cruise in *Top Gun* and so she has to remind me that Cruise was a Navy pilot and I argue that she's confusing that flick with *An Officer and a Gentleman* and then I don't remember what branch Cruise was in and my mother starts crying. I tell her she's making me feel bad and she makes herself stop.

She's pretty good about the emotional stuff. She knows when to get out of my face when she feels it coming on, it looks like to me. I'd thank her for it, but *that* would start her off, probably.

My Dad doesn't get watery-eyed. At least never in front of me. I've seen him get angry, very macho-pissed. Like with that picture-taking dude, like I said. But he never gets broken-up emotional.

He pays attention to me. I mean he talks to me and he takes me places on the weekends when he's not working overtime. But he works weekends a lot, lately. Says he can't pass up the extra money. Not when it's in-season, like now. Winter's coming fast, and my Dad thinks it's going to be snowy and cold—the reverse of the hot and dry the summer and the early fall have both been.

He tries as hard as he can and I don't hold it against him for not being around more. Because hell, the truth is he and Mom'll be around for a while, yet. They *gotta* go on living. *They* ain't going anywhere for a while yet.

He walks into my bedroom, and I turn off the Walkman and take off the earphones.

"Van Halen again? Don't you ever get tired of that tape? I'll buy you some new ones Saturday."

"I like what I've got, Dad. Haven't got time to listen to the ones I already got from the record club."

He sits down on my bed.

"Want to go to a Cubs game this weekend? I don't have to work. New job doesn't start up for a week, and then I'll be at it until the snow flies."

"Sure. Fine."

He touches my hand lightly, but his hand doesn't linger.

"Mom'll be going, too. Got box seats. From a guy at the last job. Sold 'em to me for cost."

"Great."

He wants to ask me how I'm feeling, so I help him out.

"I'm OK. Really. OK, Dad."

"Lost any more—"

"A pound. Just one pound. It's the heat, like I already told you."

"Sure. The heat. . .It's been a bitch. Only good time, even with the air conditioning on, is when the sun's going down. Like now."

I look out the window next to my bed and I see he's right.

He turns on the lamp next to my bed, then.

"Doctor, tomorrow," he reminds me.

"Why bother?"

"What do you mean, why—"

But he turns off his *macho-pissed* voice almost as quickly as he turned it on.

"They're going to cure this shit, Jay. You just gotta—"

"No they're not. Not fast enough."

"There's stuff in the paper every—"

"It's crap, Dad. You know it and I do."

"The counselor told you that hope—"

"I let go of that a while ago."

He stands up. He looks down at me, not sure whether he should be angry or sympathetic. I see things crossing his face quicker than he can handle all that traffic.

"You have to hope, Jay. It's all there is to do."

I could put on my own macho-pissed face and tell him to go to hell, that he doesn't know, nobody knows except for me. It's my *life*, and it's my—

But I don't argue.

"I hope. Sure. I *hope.*"

I turn off the lamp and the redness of sunset creeps into my bedroom. He stands in the twilight-lit room with me for a long time, but he won't look at me.

"We'll make that game in the afternoon and then we'll take in a movie at one of those fancy suburban malls after we eat a nice dinner. Your mother loves to go out for dinner."

Now he finally turns to me, and he touches my hand lightly and quickly, once more. He leaves, then, so I turn on my Van

Halen tape and I plug back in.

I'm washed in the heavy metal. The guitars sound like violins and the organ and the bass and drums sound like the rest of an orchestra. I look out my window and I see the last red rays being swallowed by the horizon, and I turn up the volume. It sounds like a symphony. *Like Beethoven gone nuts.*

I'm remembering school and Mrs. Rolinski talking about our "right to dissent" and all that colonial stuff, and I forgive her and all the other teachers for being *nice* to me. I forgive our principal, Mr. Farnsworth, for not being so nice to me. I forgive all my classmates for letting me get away with sitting by myself at lunch. I forgive my Mom for being a crybaby about all this, and I forgive my father for working all those weekends.

I even forgive the guy or woman who gave me the bogus needle at the hospital.

But I have trouble letting God off the hook for all my vampire dreams. I don't think they were really *necessary.*

I lied to my father about the weight loss. It was three pounds and not just one. And tomorrow the doctor'll make me stand on the scale and everyone'll know the truth. . .

I think the worst thing about being all alone is that it takes so long. If I got struck by lightning, it'd be over in a milli-second. But when you're alone you find yourself doing things like listening to even the most boring teachers, at school.

And I've started to listen to late-night radio, at home. You know, those talk shows. Drunks call up and try to listen to themselves on the radio. They like to hear the sound of their own voices, I guess. They ask a lot of stupid crap and they say things that are dumber than hell—

But I suppose I forgive them, too. They're just like me, in a way. They don't want to go to sleep, and neither do I.

I just don't want to say dumb things over the air and then have someone ask me, the next day, if it was me who said them.

It'll be a long night again tonight. It's not really one hundred percent dark out, yet. The sun dies hard, some nights.

I turn up my Van Halen tape. It's beating on my eardrums, but I don't care.

When the tape's over, I'll turn on one of those talk shows on

AM. They come on around nine.

My mother'll come in here to give me the goodnight kiss about ten. And naturally she'll remind me about my doctor's appointment tomorrow. But she'll leave quick because the word 'doctor' gets her teary, most of the time. She'll kiss me on the cheek twice and then she'll leave, and then I'll be alone again.

I'll listen to the radio until I finally fall asleep.

Late night radio does it to me every time.

Emma J. Blanch
Milford, CT

Yankee Thanksgiving

The brownish leaf debris
of past dreams brings
a hope for a rebirth of vitality.

We walk to the homestead
and wish for a certain newness
in spirit, that is not there.

We sigh -the duteous guests-
in knowing that nothing
will change in family ties
as long as a younger blood
is strongly kept away.

In boredom, we share the feast,
as we have done for years,
so proud of our heritage
and traditions, obsolescent in
autumnal sun of life.

Jon Sanborne
Northport, NY

Hard Winter

this was not a hard winter
for us to get through at all
we complained about a few days
of ice in the driveway
and the creak of getting
out of warm beds
and into cars
sitting in them and waiting
until the barren upholstery
softened beneath our jeans
we did hang out a few times outside
beating our hands and smoking
cigarettes in parking lots
but always with the thought
of which basement we were
going to hide away in
wrapped around a t.v. set

we complained about a few hard days
but i still remembered last year
december into january
were my warm months
a thick black dream
shared beneath the covers with you
but as we lay there
already inside
in the current of your blood stream
you knew there was no thaw waiting
for us to see together
your hands twitched
with nervous sleep
searching out new furrows
fresh holes to have dug
in time for the ground
going soft again
and my spring was blackened

(more)

with the cost of it

so this year i feel strange
even lucky
to be alone and isolated
with my friends again
beating our boots dry together
in warm buried places
talking about things
like bent fenders
we come back out of the mist
our eyes still intact
stretching our limbs
and looking around
which day was the hardest freezing
and when did it pass
with a crack and a thud
of ice sliding from the branches?
if we can't remember
then we should be thankful
that those few hard days
passed over us
as easily as they did

Rochelle Hope Mehr
West Orange, NJ

Cliffside

How did I let you slip away from me?
I was an idolator and worshipped you like heaven.
But the water, the water is such an insidious beast
Camouflaging the bronze bust I made of you with verdigris.

It is the color of the sea.
She lays claim to all who would dwarf her in prominence.
She does not simply steal — she incorporates.

You are lost to me now
And slave to that whore who floods you with her blood.
What does she ask of you?
What did you ask of her?

I shall never go playing
Cliffside anymore.

Nor shall I engage in pagan rites.

I shall be the iconoclast who loves you more for your
Humanity
Than for your perfection.

You give me a kiss.
I give you my cold.

Claire I. Wills
Fairfax Station, VA

I Have Been To Maryland

I have been to Maryland,
and I have seen the Eastern Shore,
the place where we grew up.
I have thrown stones into the water,
I have stood among the rushes,
I have looked up to the desolate sky.

Sometimes I think of Maryland,
in 1969, the time when
we were children. Enough,
just that I sense the sweetness
of another life, the prelude
of a precious place,
the hallmark of our lives.

Karin Melchoir
Bethesda, MD

Toccata And Fugue In D Minor

Johann Sebastian Bach's Tricentennial in 1985

The fugue, swift-fleeing fugitive,
rolls on and on
like pearls poured forth.
Chords rumble,
heave in longer swells,
then rise and crash
like storm-whipped breakers.

Oh, Bach, your rushing brook turned ocean
is like a tremor through the universe.

Sylvia Relation
Barre, VT

Moonflowers

Come, walk with me in the moonflowers,
        feel them knotting under our feet,
        curling together for the night.

Come, lie with me in the moonflowers,
        drinking my perfume of the night,
        and when morning sun seeps over
        we'll disappear like moonflowers
        fading into the sky.

Go,   take up your plows and harrows,
        I'll spread jam on bread
        and hang out the wash,
        while we wait for moonflowers
        to make our bed once more. . .

Sylvia Relation
Barre, VT

Two Spoons In A Drawer

Evening spreads itself
  like putty,
   slathered on the knife,
sealing the light of day,

My eyes line your back
  watching as muscles dance,

The bristles of your beard
  scraping
  across the pillow

You turn toward me
  reaching
  with calloused hands.

In the nights
  of rattling windows
and mornings calm
  with the ooze of dawn

We have lain together—
  as two spoons
  in a drawer

the swirling designs
  of your chest
  pressed to the bowl of my back,

Our patterns unmatched—
  but fitting together

Claire I. Wills
Fairfax Station, VA

The Katyn Forest

Pavlov shakes his head,
the tears are getting on his nerves.
We stand, four hours, in
freezing cold, we stand
like signposts in the darkness
of the trees; We know
which way to go.

The fear is palpable—
I hold my breath, and downward cast,
I check my line. My gun
has never failed me, yet
I can't believe I've come to this.

They tell us that we never
will reveal the secret.
Still, the forest covers just
the bitter earth, the black remains
of leaves and twigs.
It cannot, no, it will not,
petrify the biggest lie
in history: That we are victorious.
Pavlov and I are soldiers,
we will bear it bravely.

It's just that I can see them now,
nameless, faceless, helpless
baby strangers, dropping
line by line. The silence
drives me insane, and the papers
will deny it because the rulers
will deny it. We all know it,
and accept it. It's just as Pavlov says,
no-one ever can return home.

Emily W. Robinson
Kensington, MD

Wampum Water

We portaged the canoe
from lake to stream
across a sandy spit
where the tea-colored swamp water
met the crystal clear wavelets
of the big lake.

We paddled along
between birches and willows
the narrow brook
mirrored our faces
and glinted with coins
of sunlight.

We whispered for no reason
sensing a magic moment
breathing in moss fragrance
the sound of paddles dipping.

We sighted Indians
in birch canoes
searching the lowlands
for us?

Helen Engelhardt
Brooklyn, NY

Be Careful Coney Island

My grandmother let herself be seen
forever in a black satin slip
her long arms resting in her lap
her hooded eyes discerning something else.

A child's face floats above
her frizzy hair, a sinewy arm
opens a door into another room
beyond the tiled kitchen. My uncle insists
"There is no-one else in the picture but Mama."
My father, who took the picture on a summer
night, does not remember if they were alone.

There was a child with violet eyes
who died before his bris. There was a cossack
who woke them shouting at the foot
of their cowering bed. His sword slashed the air.
She ran barefooot from the room
in a white gown. Her children saw her.
Her husband could not stop her.
The soldier fled. The neighbors brought her home.
What did it take to tear her
from her father's town.

Was it so hot?
Was she so weary?
Was she so fearless
                    just this once?

Kevin J. Lavey
Baltimore, MD

Our Sessions

He lies on the floor listening to the midnight talk show host field phone calls. Love is the topic.

"Hello," says the caller to the show host, a woman. "I need some advice."

"What's on your mind?" she says.

"I think I'm in love," he says.

"How nice," she says.

"No," he says, "it's not that simple. I don't have any answers to this one. This one's got me confused."

"We all feel like that sometimes," she says.

"No," he says, "you don't feel like this sometimes."

The voices in the room with him, the darkness against the window panes, the light of the lamp. He is nailed to the floor in the deep night of summer listening to other people's problems, buoyed in a strange way by his posture of absolute surrender. He, too, is in love. A long time ago he and a woman embraced in the park near the fountain on their lunch hour. A few months later they were living together. He knew from the start that each motion they made, each step further into their involvement was done with not only love, but the idea that they were determined to succeed. That even if all other pairs of humans in the history of mankind had blundered, they would get it right.

"Why are you alone tonight?" the talk show host asks.

Well, he thinks, why is he alone? Why is he alone tonight? Yet, he is not alone: he has the radio, its voices, he has his history. He thinks of a beautiful, sustaining moment. It occurred not long ago during an afternoon of exquisite formality at her wealthy aunt's house in Boston, a visit made for obligatory reasons. His girlfriend sat across from him and he listened to her play with her voice as an actor does, an instrument of beguilement. Her aunt entertained the graces of this niece—without attending to words, speech itself—with the eyes of a drug addict, swollen, sleepy. A male companion sat smiling, enigmatic as an oriental doll. Mark had been amended to a non-entity: the aunt lived the reality of a queen, so insanely rich she was able to populate her world, or not, according to her will. She hadn't conferred upon him recognition. His girlfriend turned to him at one point and let him know through speaking eyes that he, in fact, lived immortal with her, an act which dislocated the aunt from reality, unseated her power, and moved all of them into a scene resembling the jumbled hierarchy of Alice in Wonderland. He glowed, laughed to himself, knew that never before had he been offered such a gift.

But he met this same woman on the stairway of the apartment building not four hours ago and they were strangers. "Hello," he said.

"It's an old story," the man on the radio explains. "I met a former classmate of mine."

Where was this lover, this live-in, this girlfriend of his going? He understood immediately that he was forbidden to ask. Her airs disclosed nothing. "Yes," she said, "hello."

She had a small, black leather purse under her arm. She was not in a hurry but quite obviously she carried herself with some purpose in mind; not overtly determined, but something, nonetheless, which had her distracted two points off center. Perhaps it was no more than she had received a phone call from a long ago college friend, an old roommate of hers who was passing through town who wanted to get together for a drink before she flew home. None of the particulars is disturbing. But they met awkwardly on the staircase, as though they were fellow office workers bumping into one another at a single's bar. She was dashing out and of course didn't think she'd see him. She'd left a note propped on the dial of the phone. As he was to discover, nothing in it was alarming, not one word indicating an unseen stress or pressure.

"You're out for a while, I guess," he said to her.

"Not long," she said.

She leaned to kiss him, not with warmth, but neither to signal distance or to warn him or to pass on a message of fear. The perfume she wore was fresh, rich like the scent of fur. She floated away—her hand escaping his and drifting behind her like a wind sock. Down the stairs she went, unhurriedly, her steps descending and becoming more diffuse; then the lobby door opened and slammed shut heavily. He stood in place, feeling absent to himself, his emotions unable to engage.

He lies on the floor listening to a late night talk show, visiting himself as if he were being delicately scrutinized by the talk show host. He is alone and all the world seems reduced to the poignant simplicity of unconcern. Tonight he has only life's promises of compatibility.

He listens with Hugh Patterson, the man on the line, as the talk show host tells Hugh that he has a low self-esteem—this is what she can come up with—and Mark finds out that he is a man of patience. He leads her to his real dilemma.

"I'd like her to look at me and know everything about me. I'd like her to know everything I've ever thought, I'd like somebody to know that I exist."

He must have slept because soon he is conscious of a single electronic note held constant, as if someone were pressing down the key of an electric keyboard, indicating that the station has gone off the air. In the unreality of waking he calls out the name 'Hugh.' He is certain that a kindred presence is here with him and he lingers in that belief for several moments until his head clears. He realizes there is no one. He looks up over his forehead to the door and sees that the locking chain is still in place.

He quickly understands that it's possible he's being betrayed, but that seems illogical, paranoid even. They have allowed themselves other people, with the one rule there be no deceptions. But, something, the way she held her purse on the stairway, the way her eyes were enwebbed in preoccupation and fatigue, tells him that he is truly alone, that she has begun to consider leaving.

In a moment he gets himself up off the floor, reaches for today's unread newspaper on the coffee table and goes to the kitchen. Eating a bowl of Rice Krispies he flips through the paper. A wide receiver for the Buffalo Bills is out for the season. His foot was crushed by a falling board while helping his brother build a garage. Mark has begun to feel a little better, a bit closer to himself. From the front room he hears the sound of the door opening then catching on the chain.

"Mark?" his girlfriend says. "Mark? You up?"

He listens to her voice, its sound spreading into the room and filling his ears.

"Mark? Mark! I'm locked out."

He sits quietly in his chair in the kitchen.

"Mark!" She has put her mouth close to the opening of the door.

The spoon rests in a puddle of milk at the bottom of his cereal bowl; he plays with it, stretching the watery liquid up and down.

"Mark!" Her voice is firm, determined to rouse him from sleep.

On the counter is a pack of Salems, left by a friend who visited last night. He takes a moon step over to it, chucks one out, leans to light it on the electric stove. While hovering over the burner coil, waiting for it to fire red, again he hears, "Mark!" He can picture her hesitating a moment before pulling the door shut, locking it, then walking away.

He smokes at the table. Within three minutes, his apartment phone begins chirping like a mechanical bird. The latest in designer rings, she teased him when she brought it home. The regular bird-chirp burbles for minutes and minutes while he smokes, lights another, taps the ashes in his bowl.

Rochelle Brener
Delmar, NY

Eye Of The Hurricane

You gather me into your arms
like a storm gathering its forces.
You blow across me, a dark cloud,
threatening small dangers, minor deaths,
rocking me in a roiling ocean until
wave upon wave crashes against me.
I moan, not wanting to move, unable
to stop, building a thunder
to meet your own; building slowly,
tremor by tremor. Your whispers
scream soft in my ear: teach me,
teach me — as if you were just beginning
some new meteorology. Your shoulders
are jagged rocks above me; and though
dizzy with height, I climb even higher,
seeking the source of quiet above wind,
seeking clouds that curl
like a comfort of starlight, taming
thunderheads. Explosions burst
like heat-lightning all around us,
first hitting me, then you, then me again.
We plunge through space, free-falling
together into an odd calm, a singular sea
scooped out by gently ebbing tidal currents
that contradict and repeat themselves
with exquisite power. Slowly, you gather me
into your arms, a smiling summer rain,
soft after the storm.

Phil Eisenberg
Bethesda, MD

Oblivion

You have quit the space
you once explored. . .
no more your breath intrudes
the world's domain,
your eyes no more extract
the scene. . .
How much of you vibrates
within us
as we tune our pulses
to your presence. . .
do your smiles agitate the air,
your whispers stalk our steps,
your thoughts embrace our own?
We grope for tokens of response,
but whisked from our perception,
your days unveil their fantasies,
your nights are shuttered
and sleep embraces you forever. . .

Valerie J. .
Newport, ι

Married Men

I tell them all,
These attached, wooing, gentlemen,
That I, too, turn into a wife.

They seem not to hear me,
Compare me too favorably,
Flattering me into their life.

When I question their motive,
Ask, "What's, the new notice?"
Commiserating creation persists.

They know I'm not physical,
Cynical about mystical, but
Sexuality they refuse to resist.

They think somehow a reality flight,
A new and different insight,
Guarantees kindling passion in life.

They hate my candid reminders,
That even fantasies beguiling,
Invariably, turns into a wife.

e Hyde

We need a name for when the woman does it.
We need a strategy so as not to walk away.
Spirits roam in the full white moon.
She greets us at the door, the gleaming harridin,
Who can't be reached by word or touch,
Who rips up everything the day woman nurtured,
Who stamps up stairsteps of indignation,
Then swoops down upon us,
Fearsome caped avenger,
Against the crimes of long ago.

We need to hold fire.
We need to think long term.
Before we ever came over
She sipped on her own volition
A smoking potion from a vial
That now must run its course.

In time the effects will subside.
A smile will return that promises benevolence
And to compensate for the midnight storms
Such delights of the flesh as to stir into life
The secret men we hold within.

Ron Welburn
Danbury, CT

A Woman Of Stones

We have found
a woman of stones
who has gathered us together
with steady hands
to live in her home.
On our backs she paints
stars and serpents,
faces of red lightning,
quails feet walking,
and an axe head
hurtling through the night.
Her luminous eyes bless us;
she colors us with music
and calls our markings from dreams.
Then, renewed in our lives
she dances for us,
spinning light of foot,
and we sing.

S.M. Hall, III
Portland, ME

The Curse (III)

The mouth of heaven shone its pearl like some
Toothpaste commercial. I saw thousands of
The tiny, even teeth provoked as one
To reach and fall at once, the bluish-green love
Of foaming teeth, ambitious for that smile.

"Ideal", "fabulous, glowing smile looks good
On posters, magazines" just for a while.

The world then was a polished, hard ivory.
The shining grass, the house, the pointing woods,
All reached to heaven's mouth, the care-free,
Unstained, celestial O that looked upon
This land of shining choppers, so hard won.

This place becomes a crocodile's huge maw,
And we're snapped up and mashed in her strong jaws.

Diana Azar
Irvine, CA

American Dreams

Alexis first met Richard when she was scouting properties in El Dorado for a wealthy cousin who already owned several and was eager to own more. Richard was golden-haired, much younger than Alexis, stunningly good-looking and charming. His father, an uneducated German immigrant, had made a fortune taking doctors and attorneys out to fish in the waters off Newport Beach. His modest boat eventually became a fleet, each nail of which he hammered into a parable of the Lutheran work ethic with which Richard and his older brother, already a millionaire at thirty, were raised. No scholar, Richard had dropped out of college to pursue the destiny that he was born for. "To make more money than my father. If I don't, I'll never hear the end of it, never."

Alexis took Richard home and introduced him to her husband Vic, an earthy corporate manager who worked in the nearby high-tech industrial complex. A company man all his life, Vic had got stuck in mid-management ranks, perhaps because his managerial style was overbearingly direct; perhaps because, as he himself believed, he belonged to a pre M.B.A. generation of what in El Dorado ranks was called "non-degreed personnel." He was the sort of man who taught his son to swim by throwing him into the deep end of the pool, and his methods did not set well with M.B.A.'s churned out at local universities to feed El Dorado's burgeoning corporate needs.

To show Alexis and Vic what he was up against in seeking to outdo his father's wealth, Richard took them to his parents' home in El Dorado Heights when his parents were summering at their Mexican villa in Cuernavaca, then to their bayfront house in Newport Beach, and finally to the exclusive private yacht club to which his parents belonged. Then he took them to the top of a wild ridge in the Saddleback Mountains that dwarfed El Dorado Heights in its commanding view of the valley below, and told them it was the site of his future house.

"You'll make it," Alexis said, when Richard bought his first house in Bronce Park, El Dorado's only working class tract. To make the monthly payments, he rented out two of its tiny bedrooms and even part of the garage to a homely young woman he charmed into paying almost as much as he got for the rooms. "I realize that she's ugly as sin," Richard said, whose friends all tended to be physically beautiful, "but that's a plus. My girlfriends won't get jealous." Since Bronce Park was just blocks away from modest-by-El Dorado-standards but respectable Kensington Park, where Vic and Alexis rented a house, the three became frequent visitors in each other's homes.

Alexis grew more sure of Richard's prospects than she was of Vic's. While she had once believed Vic was a diamond-in-the rough, she now half-jokingly thought of him as a zircon. Richard, who like Will Rogers had never met anyone he did not like, grew almost as attached to Vic as he soon became to Alexis, a development Alexis welcomed but had not expected. Vic had become increasingly testy as his upward mobility declined. A big man, powerfully built, he began to drink too much and to assert himself in ways Alexis found childish and inappropriate. He would challenge every male visitor to the house to arm-wrestling matches, which he invariably won, though Richard, who was slight of build and had hands and feet as small as a girl's, conceded victory before the fact, giving Vic little satisfaction. Alexis gave up racquetball, her favorite sport, after Vic, avenging an especially tricky return she'd made, slammed back a deliberately placed, vicious shot that hit Alexis in the face, sent her glasses flying, knocked her to her knees, and left a permanent mark on her cheek.

When Richard sold his tiny Bronce Park house to Alexis' rich cousin and bought a better one in Kensington Park just a block away, Vic overheard him mention to Alexis that his racquetball game was improving. He challenged Richard, who had taken up the sport at Vic's suggestion, to a match.

Richard good-naturedly accepted; unlike Alexis, whose hand inadvertently rose to her cheek, Richard at first did not give Vic's challenge much thought. He and Alexis continued their talk of property values and money, while Vic, more interested in sport, drifted off to watch McEnroe and Connors in another room.

Richard's increasingly frequent visits gratified and disturbed Alexis. She was touched by Richard's openness, the eager intensity with which he shared his American dream, his dogged determination to succeed, and the integrity which Richard never compromised, not even when it cost him money. Alexis backed out of a real estate deal for her cousin after Richard, acting as agent and in desperate need of the commission to seal his Kensington Park purchase, pointed out a drawback about the property that she herself had failed to see. Though Richard liked to discuss all his business dealings with Alexis, almost as if she were his wife, he was more experienced in business than Alexis, and she soon learned from him something she never could have learned from Vic—that a good business deal is not one in which any party loses but rather one in which all parties win.

"Bullshit," was Vic's response to Richard's definition of good deals. Alexis watched him pour himself another Scotch on the rocks. He'd been passed over again for promotion and was in no mood for Dale Carnegie twaddle.

"It's different in the corporate world," Alexis said in an attempt to mediate between Richard's untarnished vision and Vic's. "A lot of people compete for one job, and everyone loses except the one who gets it."

"Invariably an asshole," Vic said. "A suckbutt." He sank into the chair no one sat in but he and moodily swirled his Scotch on the rocks.

Richard handed Alexis an envelope and said, "Count it."

"Why?" said Alexis. "If you say it's there, it's there."

"Hey, hey," said Vic. "What the hell's going on?"

"He went for it," Alexis said, picturing their ten-year-old son with braces. "Colin bought Richard's Kensington Park house."

Alexis had explained it all to Vic before, but Vic had either forgotten or not logged what she said. Richard had an opportunity to buy a house in upscale Casa de California for ten thousand under its market price. To consummate the deal, he had to sell his Kensington Park house at once. He offered Alexis a thousand dollars if she could interest her cousin or anyone else in buying his Kensington Park house. His terms of sale were so attractive, Alexis called her cousin at once. Richard would find a new tenant, make good on any delinquent rent for a year, and even maintain the grounds. Alexis did not have to sell Colin on anything; the deal spoke for itself.

Vic bit into an ice cube, splitting it in half. "You moving already again? Where to this time, El Dorado Heights?"

Richard smiled. "Casa de California is three, probably four moves from The Heights."

"You gonna have the gate guard say Vic Who when I come by?"

"No," Richard said. "You know I'm not like that."

"There *are* no gate guards in Casa de California," Alexis said.

"Colin know about that?" Vic asked Alexis.

"Know about what?" Alexis said.

"The fee for your enthusiasm. Your kickback."

"You guys want to have dinner at Sizzler? Great salad bar. $4.99 apiece—I've got a coupon."

"My enthusiasm was sincere," Alexis said. "In fact Richard gave Colin too good of a deal. You did, you know. The yard was too damn much. Colin would've gone for it even without the yard."

"Just how sincere was it?" Vic pointed a thick, inflexible finger at the bulging envelope Alexis held in one hand and stroked with the other, as she often did their cat and son but had not done for Vic since his racquetball hit her in the face.

"Colin's forever telling me my business head is as soft as my heart. He never lets me close a deal. He says I'll never be successful in business as long as I want to be loved more than I want to be rich. I give too much, he says. I don't know how to take. If he knew about this"—she held up the envelope—"he'd be pleased."

Vic scoffed. "Then why don't you tell him?"

"I don't want him to think the information that I give him is in any way influenced by self-interest. Because it's not."

"I'm gonna kick your ass all the way from here to El Dorado Heights," Vic said and knocked his empty glass off the arm of his chair.

"Why?" said Alexis, who was not sure whose ass Vic referred to but, out of politeness, assumed it to be her own. "'Cause now we can get Brian's teeth fixed?"

Vic's finger pointing at Richard reminded Alexis of Uncle-Sam Wants-You wartime posters from a previous era. "I'm giving you a month. To practice night and day, not that it's gonna do you any good."

Richard eyed Vic's well-defined serving arm bicep and pictured Vic reeling hundred-pounders into a rusty boat before an audience of Sunday fishermen. He himself did not fish; he sailed. "How 'bout the seafood special?" he said with a winning smile. "The coupon's good for everybody in the party."

"I have a problem with Casa de California," Richard said to Alexis two weeks later while Vic stared with one open eye into the darkening amber fluid at the bottom of his glass.

"That's two whole problems for you in a month," Vic said.

Alexis played dove to Vic's crow as Richard explained that the seller of the Casa de California house he'd bought had been killed in an auto accident and his wife, although the property was already in Escrow, now wanted to keep the house after all.

"I told her I'd already sold Kensington Park and that the new buyer had leased it to another tenant."

"You have a tenant for Colin already?" Alexis said. "I'm impressed."

"You'll never get past my first serve," said Vic.

Richard looked anxious. "I leased the house to Ugly-As-Sin. She's had it with the garage."

"Three fifty a month for a garage shared with your car," said Vic. "You could sell hammers and sickles to J. Edgar Hoover."

"The widow begged me to let her back out. She cried." Richard, whose business principles only allowed for winners, met Alexis' eyes with a self-doubt she'd never seen in them before.

"Give alms to the poor," Vic said. "Comfort the widow in her affliction."

"What did you say?" Alexis asked.

Richard pleaded his "no" before Alexis as if she were a judge. In concluding, he said, "She's taking me to court."

"That's two of us," Vic said. "I'm going to wipe the racquetball court with your ass."

"You'll win," Alexis said. "But where will you live till this comes to trial?"

"Here?" Vic inquired. "I'll let you have the broom closet for just a thousand bucks a day.''

"Where I am," Richard said. "Karla's going to let me stay."

"Ugly-As-Sin's in love with you," said Vic, pouring himself another drink. He looked Alexis in the eye. "Just like everyone else."

"What would you do in my place?" Richard asked Alexis.

"Wrong question," said Alexis, who always found it easier to take the part of others than to take her own. "You can't be penalized because her husband died. Colin says to be successful in business, your head has to rule your heart."

"Throw the grieving widow and her kids into the street?" said Vic. "I'm going to wipe the court with your hard-hearted ass."

"She has no kids," Richard said as he rose to go.

"And even if she did," Alexis said, although she knew in Richard's place she would back down. "Stay for dinner. I won't take no for an answer."

"No," Richard said, "I can't."

Alexis walked Richard to his baby blue Cadillac in the waning Southern California light. She saw the racquet and tin of three balls lying on the front seat and decided to take no for an answer.

Alexis had been married to Vic a long time and felt forever bound to him through their son Brian. Her outward behavior toward him changed little though she no longer loved him and supposed he knew it. Alexis did not think you could fool people into thinking they were loved if they were not, or not loved if they were. Her loyalty to Vic was like that of a nun who remains true to vows and habit after she has lost her faith. God, if there was a god, would not be fooled for duty is a loveless substitute for faith.

Alexis dutifully concealed her scorn for Vic's browbeating, bullying of Richard, not only from Richard and Vic but from herself. As the day of the match approached, Vic unrelentingly reminded Richard of his physical inferiority, asserting that Richard was not and never would be half the man he was, no matter where he lived in El Dorado, and glancing scornfully at Richard's small hands and feet. Vic's golf and tennis trophies, consigned to a box in the garage, suddenly reappeared. As Vic recounted details of past victories to Richard, he made it clear that he would not be content just to win; his competitive lust required that his opponent be annihilated. When he played racquetball with his ten-year-old son, Alexis made Brian wear a face-mask because the moment he successfully returned a ball, Vic smashed it back, "to keep him from getting ideas." If Alexis complained, her hand unconsciously rising to the mark on her cheek, Vic's reply was, "That's what it's like out there. He might as well get that straight now."

"Shouldn't you be practicing?" Alexis asked Vic a week before the match.

"What for?" Vic took her hand, placed it on his stomach and flexed. "Feel that," he said, then guided her hand lower down. "Richard thinks I'm a loser because I'm old enough to be his father and I'll never live in El Dorado Heights. But I'm a natural. There's no way he can compete with that."

"Since when's racquetball played with that?"

"All competitive games are played with that."

The day before the match Alexis sat alone on the love seat, watching Richard silently bear Vic's taunts. His barbs became so pointed, Alexis, who'd been careful to maintain outward neutrality, could barely restrain herself from answering back on Richard's behalf, but restrain herself she did, as Richard did, both enduring Vic's goads in silence because both knew he would probably win. The tension in the room grew so intense, Alexis marvelled it did not get up and shout and flail its arms.

As she walked Richard to his car, she looked down at a crimson spray of bottlebrush, dropped from the towering tree above. "Tomorrow," she said. "I hope. . ." Her voice trailed off.

"Has Vic ever hit you?" Richard suddenly asked.

"Not really," said Alexis, deciding those two times and the one with the racquetball didn't count. "He just throws fits and makes loud threats."

When Richard made a fist, his small hand drew from Alexis a resigned sigh. When his fist opened to expose a palm coarse with calluses, Alexis's mouth opened too but could not speak. Instead she stooped, picked up a crimson bottlebrush blossom from the cement under their feet and pressed it into Richard's hand.

"You coming?" Vic asked Alexis as Richard waited in Vic's car, his racquet spread across legs naked but for a thin cover of blond hair.

"No," said Alexis. "I can barely stand it from here."

"Stand what?" Vic said. "You never back me up. You take everyone's side but mine."

Alexis did not answer.

"Aren't you going to wish me luck?"

Alexis looked at Vic's broad chest, his massive hand choking the racquet's neck. "I don't believe in luck," Alexis said. "I don't believe in anything."

She was still sitting alone in the love seat over an hour later when she sensed, among other things, Vic's return. Through stuccoed walls, the closed garage door and the back door that led into the kitchen, his shame invaded Alexis's every cell. He appeared in the hallway, drenched in sweat, his racquet dangling idly at his side. They looked at each other for what seemed a long time before he turned away. She heard the ice and slosh and then the mixing stick against the glass.

Alexis rose and went into the bedroom. An atheist who'd substituted belief in romantic love for God, she fell to her knees by the bed, hands clasped as if in prayer and chanted, "Thank you thank you thank you," over and over again. She did not hear the door open behind her.

"What're you doing?" Vic asked.

"I'm looking for my shoes."

"What's wrong with the pair on your feet?"

"My tennis shoes," Alexis said, finding them and putting them on. She brushed past her husband, retrieved the racquet and tin of balls from the counter where he'd left them and strode out of the house, slashing air with the racquet as she went.

Jean Junge
White Plains, NY

After A May Rain Storm

Late in a day of winds and rain
The sun bursts on a washed world.
People and cars venture into the sparkle
Of newgreen trees and shrubs.
A breeze stirs rain-soaked lilac clusters,
The garden is a many-colored rug of tulip petals.
The sun dries pinched-together petunia trumpets.
Unblinking in the downpour, the star-eyed
Crimson azalea stares boldly at the sky.
The evergreens disply their lettuce green
Fingertips like nailpolish.
The Japanese cherry showers
Petaldrifts on the driveway.
As if a pail of water had been splashed
In their faces, houses wear a surprised
Look of Spring.

Mariquita Platov
Tannersville, NY

Contadora

Conscience spells out the Manahatta mix.
The cataclysmic lineaments are harsh
incised into the concrete, and they stare.
The squares of blood, the thorns of flesh think loud.
Torture down the Avenue of A's,
the swindle chain forged agelong link by link
climaxes, and imports its countries whole.
Fierce hearthstone, resonant with karmic din!
Snug in her stepdame's eminent domain,
    "First kill yourselves!" she crows, "Then we will talk."
Seared to the grid, hard nailed percussion fast,
Dolores has to listen. She reflects:
"Out of such rivets and wringings, what reward?"
To be this woman is a flagrant thing.

Rena Rosenwasser
Berkeley, CA

Marmor

— I am Marmor. Once I was perpulchur.
From Pavonazetto I came with my green and violet
veins.

A background, a surface, there the rock
matter, materia was me.

Cool to the touch a face chiseled
against my varied, vivid veins. Where shape
and volume given
became a life that was my own.

Now I am placed to rest.

Murmur of memory amidst the shards—
a cracked slab of marble
under vacant ash and voluminous
volcanic dust.

John K. Ottley, Jr.
Atlanta, GA

A February Night

On a February night
a cold wind blows
in long even breaths
the gods coax fire
from the coals of my dreams.
Come, night wind
come, fierce breath of arctic gods
scatter my thoughts of her
as dry leaves
lifted high toward glowing stars
in a black cloudless sky
so that some
in falling
may touch my lover
as she sleeps
on a February night.

Helen Engelhardt
Brooklyn, NY

Winter Solstice

The winter solstice of my 40th year
the sun did not show its face to us
at all.
The turning point occured at 6:10.
By calm astronomical reckoning it arrived
as far south as it can ever reach
and stood still. All this was
hidden from our eyes by clouds and sleep.
When we woke from lurid forgotten dreams
we listened to voices beamed through the air
and bathed and went about our business.
This birthday of the gods of another antique
time - Zeus, Dionysus, Apollo,
Mithras, and by Church decree in 273 (A.D.)
of Joshua the Nazarene - this day when the druid
cut the mistletoe, I bought bunches
of holly and pine, the Joy of Cooking,
a wooden roller for my spine,
a turtleneck for my husband, a calendar
of celestial influences for 1980,
put up fliers announcing the Solstice
Poetry Series all over the eastern
edge of Seventh Avenue, cooked
supper, phoned a friend, lit
a candle and thought about the sun.

Scott Sonders
Sherman Oaks, CA

Melted Diamonds

the frenzy of crickets
exploded
in the hot night
undiluted by darkness
and the sky
was transparent obsidian
swirling with stars
that seemed
as melted diamonds

and those diamonds
stay transfused
in my veins
with every memory
of the skin round
her breasts pressed
so hard to my ribs
that i saw
how first adam felt
when god cleaved
eve from his side
and their bodies then
forever hungered
to rejoin.

Bernard Forer
Sarasota, FL

Forgotten Songs

My dear wife's mother was a little sparrow.
Her broad Slavic face was punctuated
By amazing blue-blue eyes.
She had lived through many travails in the old country
But now she showed hardly a wrinkle.
When she was very old
She skittered around her daily tasks
Hummng and singing sad-sweet songs
Of her youthful days.
Some of the melodies haunted me,
Familiar and yet unknown,
Chronicling better times and long-gone joys.
Now I am eighty-one
And I find myself humming songs from the 1930's
Unconsciously.

Aubrey E. Nolte
Allen Park, MI

A Search For O'Day

The trip from Metamora to Bear Island was sure a drain upon the old body resources. Why did we go?

Little did I know there were alligators lurking behind the stump. After rowing for a while and long before we'd ever get to the Island shore I'd cut the engine and just glided through the water by oar. It had been out of gear for awhile and was idling.

Amy said, "It'll probably just be all sand when we get to the Island. I don't like to fish anyway. If I'd known it would be like this, I'd just as soon stayed home. We don't have anything to eat." All these barriers for staying had to be released a little by each trip.

You could hear the oars enter the water. Kersloop, kersloop, and a splash against the side of the boat if we hit broadside into a wave.

She was just sitting in the boat on the little stained and frayed blanket that was her constant companion when we were away from the house. It had made many trips with her in summer, and her mother stayed home.

I cautioned Amy to remain seated while I went on deck to get jackets for us both to wear. Our safety collars had been on before leaving shore, but now the air chilled down. A lack of activity for us both caused a need for heavier clothing.

The trolling lines were set and no activity had been noticed on the bait for a quarter mile or more. We were trolling to the Island and going for a supply of cut fire logs.

Our radio was still blaring away with news and cowboy hits by the real country singers.

Jason was still asleep and sat up on the bedside, when I swung the door shut before taking the heavier clothes with me.

"I think it was O'Day," she said. It was at the planned dinner gathering on the day before our departure for the Island. A lady I'd known long before planned what seemed to be just a chance meeting when we entered the restaurant. They came to talk awhile just as we were getting ready to eat.

I'd said, "There's plenty of room, we can all eat here." I thought if my old employee and I ate more together we may be able to talk out what she meant by the word O'Day. At the same time she said, "O'Day," her husband had said, "It was in 1959, that we did the work together." It wasn't quite clear if she was finishing up a conversation with her husband, or if she was talking to me.

I said, "How are you folks anyway, we haven't talked in so long?" Just stalling for time to figure out what she meant.

Not really knowing what else to say to try and draw them out at such a hasty meeting, I pointed to the salad bar. We had gathered close enough to almost reach the plates and silver. Time wasted.

I looked at the small boy standing by their side, who was dressed in exquisite fabric, a pin striped suit and tie. His shoes were polished, his hair loosly combed.

Just as she repeated what I'd thought she said earlier, "I think it really was O'Day," he said, "That's our grandson."

"It still wasn't clear who she was talking to.

I found out later that the boy at their side was an adopted grandson. Their daughter's natural born son was soon to die of cancer unless a miracle of remission was to happen.

Jason has overheard the whole conversation and filled me in just a little bit. He knew about the tragedy that was unfolding in their life. There had been prayer meetings, and the doctor had done all that was humanly possible. The rest, as they say, will have to be up to the acts of the gods.

But she seemed to be working upon another project!

I'd known long before she was interested in conversion, but this was much different it seemed, and so direct as if there was some other emergency than the health of the real grandson.

I knew she was sincere so our chance conversation had been numberous when we had worked together before. Relaxed, and at mealtime.

The boat was riding smoothly and I could guide it easily. Jason picked slightly at the corners of first one eye and the other to remove the last remnants of the three hour sleep he'd just completed. He had just come from the cabin. He washed up and started to prepare breakfast, so we could eat our late morning meal on the boat before sighting shore.

The easel was sitting on the picnic table that Jason had

brought along for his amusement and occupation on the trip. He'd planned while finishing school for this to be his vacation before going to his first real job.

We'd finished our cabin the year before at the Island station and put in a one way phone so we'd not be disturbed. The radio would konk out too in another half mile. Then we'd be free of mankind for the two days, while I loaded the wood for the return trip. Only us three and our picnic lunch.

As soon as we'd hit shore, Amy was totally occupied by her own actions. The Island was the same as a huge sand box for her. She'd even left her blanket lay for a morning at a time all by itself on the sandy beach.

While carrying out the gang plank to load the wood by, I mentioned the word "O'Day" to Jason to get some understanding, but he never mentioned who it might've been she was alluding to. There wasn't really any way to open the conversation all over again, and get the channel I thought she was on. Some things have to go unsaid, so we let it drop, for then.

Winter would set in soon and the water would be partially frozen if we waited many more weeks for the next trip. I'd gotten wood on line during summer cuttings for the heating season.

Jason found his favorite log to sit upon and started some sketching.

"Take your time," I said, "and paint them out now while you can still get the colors to match up." The leaves would be falling soon and all the bright colors gone.

Now the boat was listing slightly in a strong wind as I walked back and forth almost in a trot to load the boat, just so I could have the rest of the evening to myself to make sense of the conversation before I forgot it.

There seemed to be such an urgency at the end of the salad bar when we'd talked. If only I could think it through while Jason and I were away. But my old employers were not on the Island, and now the circumstances were different.

But as they say history does repeat itself, there seems to be no way to look up the answer to her proposed question, and it seemed like there was no way to question her further.

Amy finished her first long play spell alone on the white sandy beach. Her young body came flying through the air toward the boat. Her footsteps sprayed sand in both directions. Her arms grabbed me around the neck and we embraced.

"Jason and I want to go back and get mother," she said. Her look-alike brother was closing the paint box. He rose to compare what he'd just done to the landscape before we left for home. The winds had died down now that it was near dusk, I started the engine for the trip.

Our solitude was soon broken when leaving the Island, the thump of a guitar and fiddle soon broke in on the radio when we got out from the high embankment that shielded us. I cast out the troll line for the return journey. Pike may still be taking the bait, I thought. The kids sat down by the arched rod and I went to prepare for our arrival back home.